SOU

Her father had prized freedom above
all else, but the irony of it was, that her
father's last few days of freedom had
cost Vanessa her own. Her passion for
Raoul had trapped her, and there
seemed to be no alternative but to agree
to his suggestion . . .

Books you will enjoy
by KAY THORPE

THE INHERITANCE

Although Eve and her sister Fleur were
thrilled beyond words when an unknown aunt
left them a ranch in Florida and a lot of
money to go with it, they could not agree on
what to do with the property: Fleur was all for
selling it, Eve wanted to live there and run it
herself. But no way was she going to allow
their overbearing neighbour Brett Hanson
to make up her mind for her!

NO GENTLE PERSUASION

'It will save a lot of time if I tell you I'm
prepared to do anything you want to get my
father off the hook.' If Lauren had known
exactly what situation that statement would
land her in, would she have made it?

DOUBLE DECEPTION

Forced to impersonate her twin sister, Gail
had to pretend at one moment to be the
unscrupulous Karen, and then revert to being
her own less brittle self. And all because of
one man—Luke Prentis!

SOUTH SEAS
AFFAIR

BY

KAY THORPE

MILLS & BOON LIMITED
15–16 BROOK'S MEWS
LONDON W1A 1DR

First published in Great Britain 1985 by Mills & Boon Limited

© Kay Thorpe 1985

Australian copyright 1985 Philippine copyright 1985 This edition 1985

ISBN 0 263 75209 7

Set in Monophoto Plantin 10 on 11 pt. 01–1185 – 53630

Made and printed in Great Britain by Richard Clay (The Chaucer Press) Ltd, Bungay, Suffolk

CHAPTER ONE

HE had joined the flight at Singapore, this man Vanessa kept catching glimpses of through the reflective perspex of the port. For the past hour he had been concentrating on some kind of paperwork, the let-down table in front of him piled with sheets already perused. More first-class than tourist she had thought when he had come along the aisle in the wake of the other boarding passengers. His clothes, his bearing, the touch of arrogance in the tilt of his head, they all suggested a man of means. Meeting the vivid blue eyes for that fleeting moment as he murmured a polite greeting before taking his seat at her side, she had felt the sudden prickle at the nape of her neck as if the hair itself had lifted. Such instant antipathy was outside her experience: there was no reasoning behind it. Even now she felt hemmed in by his presence.

Resolutely, she turned her thoughts to other matters, recalling Michael's face when they had said goodbye at Heathrow. He loved her, she knew, in his own way, but was it in hers? What could she want from a man that Michael could not give her? It was an unanswerable question because she wasn't even sure what was missing. Time was what she had needed, and time was what she was claiming. If she were totally honest with herself, that had been one of the deciding factors in taking this trip at all.

Her father had still been alive and well a year ago, that much she knew from his last letter tucked away in her flight bag. She had written to the *poste restante* address to tell him of her mother's death in a road accident only days after it had happened back in September, but had received no reply. He might even have left New Caledonia for good, Michael had pointed out, trying to dissuade her, but it had not undermined her resolve. She would search until she found him, or until the funds she had allocated to the trip ran too dangerously low for comfort, whichever came first. At least she would have made the effort.

Looking back now, she could recall only vague detail. She had only been seven years old when he had left home. Even before that he had been away a lot, travelling in his job. 'Itchy feet', her mother had said sadly once. 'He always had itchy feet. I knew it when I married him.' It had been a long time before Vanessa was of an age to count dates and realise what else her mother had known at the time. Younger by twelve years than the man she had married, she had also been pregnant by him.

He had tried, there was no doubt. For almost eight years he had stood by his word. Trying to understand, Vanessa supposed that at forty-two he had felt life was passing him by too quickly to waste any more time. He had at least been able to leave his wife and child reasonably well-provided for. That fact alone would have helped still any pangs of conscience. Now, sixteen years later, Vanessa had purged herself of any lingering resentment. She simply wanted to see him again, to get to know him. He was her father still when all was said and done. That had to mean something.

Michael had been against selling the house, but the decision had been hers to make. Even if she did eventually marry him, she wouldn't want to live in it with him. Not that she had been unhappy during the years she had spent growing up there, but she and her mother had never been particularly close. Perhaps subconsciously, the latter had blamed her for the break-up of her marriage, yet from what she did know of her father, Vanessa doubted if there would have been any marriage at all under other circumstances. The sale had realised enough to make this trip feasible and still leave a good round sum to be added to those investments already inherited, so whatever happened the future was fairly secure. Giving up her job had been the biggest wrench, yet she could hardly expect it kept open for an indefinite period. If she married Michael on her return she wouldn't need a job anyway, because he didn't like the idea of a working wife unless her contribution was essential to household economy. That attitude was part of the problem, Vanessa was bound to acknowledge. She wasn't sure she could settle to just being a wife.

She dozed off somewhere over Borneo, still weary after the previous day's flight from Paris. The light touch of a hand on her arm woke her with a start some unknown time later. When she turned her head she found herself looking directly into those disturbing blue eyes again.

'They're starting to serve dinner,' he said. 'I thought you might regret missing it if you were left to sleep. Was I right?'

Vanessa pulled herself together, stifling the impulse to reach up and run a hand over her hair as she sat up straighter in her seat. 'Thank you,' she said. 'I'm not exactly starving at the moment but I probably would have been by the time the next meal comes round. What is it, do you know?'

His mouth took on a slant. 'We have a choice between chicken tandoori and steak, it seems. I'd advise the steak.'

She glanced his way again, taking in the cut of hard-boned features, the dark thickness of his hair. Mid-thirties, she reflected irrelevantly, and sure of his ground. Her nape was prickling as before, yet with a subtle difference in effect. She said quickly, 'You fly this route often, *monsieur*?'

His smile was fleeting yet it altered his whole face, sending a sudden frisson the length of her spine. 'My accent is so noticeable?'

'Scarcely at all,' she acknowledged. 'But as we're on our way to French territory it seemed a fair chance. You *are* French?'

'A Frenchman who never lived in France,' he acknowledged without particular regret. 'Very rarely even visited it, in fact. There have been DuTemples on *Calédonie* since the collapse of the Paris Commune last century. Thousands were exiled, although most returned after the amnesty in eighteen-seventy-nine.'

'But not the DuTemples.'

'Not then, not since.' He was openly appraising her face beneath its aureole of red-brown curls, dwelling on the curve of her mouth, the stubborn jut of her chin; lifting to scan the sea-green eyes that were her only real claim to beauty. 'My name is Raoul,' he added. 'And yours?'

The paperwork had been put away, which meant he was probably bored enough to be seeking diversion, Vanessa told herself drily, trying not to respond to the interest with too much enthusiasm. Here was a man who had no doubt made an art of drawing out a woman to talk about herself—a man who could set hearts fluttering all over the place with just one of those smiles of his. Typically French, she wouldn't know, because he was the first of his race she had actually met, but he certainly epitomised the popular concept.

'Vanessa,' she said. 'Vanessa Grantham.'

His expression altered suddenly, brows drawing together a little. 'Grantham?' he repeated. 'That's a common name in your country?'

'Not so very.' She was disconcerted by the switch in mood. 'Why?'

'Why are you visiting Caledonia?' he countered on the same altered note.

She hesitated only briefly before making the decision. The name had meant something to him, that was apparent, and she was probably going to need help anyway. 'I'm going to see my father,' she admitted. 'Neal Grantham. Do you know him?'

This time his expression revealed little. 'He's expecting you?'

There was no point in lying about it. Vanessa shook her head. 'No, he isn't. I'm planning on surprising him.' She paused, waiting, perturbed by his continuing silence. 'You didn't answer my question,' she reminded him at length.

'I know him.' The tone was short, lacking any trace of its former indulgence. 'Too well.'

So he was still on the island, she thought in relief, momentarily ignoring the naunces in that latter statement. A year was a long time. Anything could have happened. Her companion was leaning back in his seat again looking suddenly remote, but she could hardly leave it there.

'I gather you don't feel too well disposed towards him,' she said. 'Would you mind explaining why? I haven't seen him in sixteen years.'

The dark head didn't turn. 'Which might explain how it is that no one ever heard about you before. Don't you think it would have been a better idea to write first and make sure he wanted to see you?'

Michael had said much the same thing; she made the same answer. 'I didn't intend giving him the chance to say no.'

'I see. Present him with a *fait accompli* and hope for the best.' His upper lip had curled a little. 'You may find that wasn't such a wise move.'

'I know it wasn't a wise move,' Vanessa acknowledged doggedly. 'If I had any real sense I wouldn't be here at all—I've heard it all before. The point is he *is* my father, and I want to see him again. What he does about it is something else.'

'True.' Raoul DuTemple inclined his head. 'I wish you luck.'

The stewardess arrived with their trays, murmuring something in French as she slid Raoul's in front of him. Vanessa's grasp of the language was just about good enough to make out that she was apologising for the lack of space up front in first-class. 'My own fault,' he replied. 'I arrived late.' Obviously a regular customer, Vanessa reflected, looking without interest at her own tray. He was giving every indication that the conversation was finished so far as he was concerned. So be it. Whatever it was he had against her father she would prefer not to hear it anyway. More than anything, she needed a completely open mind.

The hours passed slowly. Vanessa slept and woke, and slept again, tucking herself down into the corner of her seat with her pillow jammed between the seatback and bulkhead and the blanket pulled well up around her. Wakening for the second time when they finally caught up with the dawn, she found the seat beside her empty, and took the opportunity to make her own foray to the rear facilities.

Raoul DuTemple was on his way back down the aisle from the front of the plane as she returned. Taller than she would have anticipated in a male of his race, his body looked lean and supple in the lightweight slacks and bush shirt for which he had exchanged his suit. He had shaved too, she noted. A devastatingly attractive man, she was bound to acknowledge. That hadn't been antipathy she had felt in those first moments of meeting, just pure and simple chemistry at work.

'First-class privileges if not space?' she commented with faint irony as he paused to allow her time to slide into her seat ahead of him. 'You must be a valuable customer, *monsieur*.'

'So you understand French,' he said, ignoring the gibe. 'Do you speak the language too?'

'Well enough to get by if needs be. I understood English was widely used on New Caledonia?'

'Since the tourists started coming in it's been necessary, but French is the main language still.' His glance went to the port with its view of endless white cloud and high blue sky. 'Two more hours and we'll be there. First breakfast, and then we start the descent. The cloud will begin to clear now we've left the mainland behind. If you never visited Australia before, you should try making a stopover on your way home. You'd find it well worth while.'

Vanessa said softly, 'You're so sure I'll be going home?'

He looked at her then, a long hard look. 'There's nothing for you on *Calédonie*. You'll discover that soon enough. Your father . . .' He paused, lifting his shoulders. 'You must judge for yourself.'

Vanessa was silent for several moments. Even if he could be persuaded to tell her what he knew, was it fair to her father to ask? Raoul DuTemple was his enemy, there was nothing surer than that. His opinion had to be biased to start with.

'You can at least tell me where to find him,' she said at length. 'I only have a *poste restante* address.'

'I'll drop you off myself at the quay,' he responded without inflection.

'The quay?'

'He lives aboard his boat.'

Vanessa was unable to conceal her disconcertion. 'You mean he's a fisherman?'

'Not in quite the way I think you mean. The *Julia* is used for charter. She's an excellent craft.' The irony was unmistakable. 'There's no shortage of work, I can assure you.'

He said no more, but he had given her plenty to think about. Fishing—no matter how up-market—and what she knew of her father somehow didn't go together. He was a qualified engineer, with degrees in both metallurgy and mineralogy. Having read something of the economy of New Caledonia, she had naturally assumed he would be involved in the nickel mining which provided more than ninety per cent of the island's export income. Yet why make assumptions after sixteen years? He would be in his mid-fifties now. Perhaps he'd grown tired of covering the same ground. Fishing would be an excellent way of easing himself into retirement, especially if it paid well. It wasn't as if she had expected him to provide her with a place to stay. All she wanted was to see him again.

As Raoul had promised, the cloud cover broke up during the following hour or so. The first sight of the island was stupendous, the strange colours of the mineral deposits streaking the double chain of mountain peaks that formed its spine as if stroked on by brush. Wooded lower slopes reached out arms into the sea. Some miles offshore the encircling reef glowed jade and turquoise in a limpid ocean.

Pure white beaches fringed by coconut palms came into view as the aircraft lost height, the former sloping gently into the shallow waters of the great lagoon. Island of light, the French called it. It looked a South Seas paradise.

Only when they were down and in the airport itself did she begin to realise how complex a population the island held. White skins mingled with brown and black and every shade between, the womens' clothing ranging from the most up to date European right through to the Indonesian sarong. Gendarmes in kepis and shorts ushered the new arrivals through formalities with a welcome lack of complication.

Raoul had a car waiting. Seated beside him in the luxuriously appointed, air-conditioned interior, Vanessa wondered what he did for a living. While the *Société le Nickel* appeared to hold the monopoly where mining was concerned, she was aware that the island also had some independent operators—most of them, by all accounts, millionaires. Not that it made any great difference to her what or who he was, she told herself flatly. She would hardly be seeing him again.

Banana and breadfruit grew alongside the road into Noumea, fringing a gently undulating landscape covered in eucalyptus. Colour abounded in the gardens of the long, low bungalows on the outskirts of the capital—scarlet poinsettia mingled with the startling pinks of hibiscus, the vibrant yellow of allamanda. Traffic was heavy. Avoiding the main stream, Raoul took to the narrow back streets where bougainvillaea and honeysuckle spilled over high stone walls, twisting and turning until Vanessa lost all sense of direction. It was almost eleven by the time they reached the busy waterfront. Raoul brought the car to a stop along a quayside, getting out to swing Vanessa's suitcase from the boot.

'The *Julia* is berthed down along there,' he said, indicating the nearest of the long, wooden walkways. 'Forgive my lack of gallantry. Your father would be no more delighted to see me than I would him. If you need a hotel I can recommend Le Belvedere.'

'Thanks, I'll remember.' She took the suitcase from him, her smile over-bright. 'You've been very helpful.'

'The least I could do.' The slant of his lips underlined the ambiguity of that statement. He gave her one last fleeting scrutiny, then got back into the car.

Vanessa turned away before he was out of sight, smoothing her beige linen skirt down over slim hips with her free hand as she looked out across the thronged craft. She had travelled halfway around the world for this moment, yet now that it was on her she scarcely knew *what* she wanted anymore. Sixteen years was a long time—perhaps too long. Both her advisors had been right. She should have written first.

But she hadn't, and she was here, and there was only one way she was going to find out if she had made a mistake, she told herself resolutely. It was too late to turn back now.

The boardwalk was long, and not exactly stable. Making her way down it, Vanessa wished she had had the forethought to change her footwear before venturing forth. The heels of her sandals were hardly suited to this kind of terrain. Somebody whistled from one of the boats as she stumbled over an uneven board, bringing a flush to her cheeks. Where on earth was the *Julia*!

She found it at last right down near the end of the walkway, a sleek white craft sitting high in the water. One of the swivel chairs bolted to the after deck was occupied at present by a fair-haired young man clad in a pair of tattered shorts. He had his feet propped along the rail, his clasped hands supporting the back of his head in an attitude of total relaxation.

'*Je* ... er ... *cherche, Monsieur* Grantham,' Vanessa said hesitantly, and saw the man's eyes pop open as his head swung sharply her way.

'Hey, you're English!' he exclaimed, propelling himself to his feet. 'I'd know that accent anywhere!'

His enthusiasm was catching. Vanessa found herself grinning back. Lean as a greyhound, and tanned the colour of well-done toast, he was probably little more than a couple of years older than her own twenty-three. 'I just got in this morning,' she acknowledged. 'I came straight from the airport.' She paused, brows lifting inquiringly. 'This *is* Neal Grantham's boat?'

'Yes, it is.' Curiosity sprang alive in his eyes. 'Do you know him?'

'He's my father,' she said.

The shock was evident. Whole seconds passed before he said slowly, 'I didn't know he even had a daughter.'

Vanessa shrugged, sensing the doubt. 'You don't have to take my word for it. He'll verify it himself. Is he on board?'

'Yes.' He made a visible effort to pull himself together, glancing briefly for'ard then back to her face with every sign of discomfiture. 'Only you can't see him right now. He's ... asleep.'

'At this time of the morning?' Watching the play of expression across the pleasantly open features, Vanessa knew a sudden alarm. 'He's not ill, is he?'

'No.' The sigh held a note of resignation. 'You'd better come aboard.'

He stashed her suitcase inside the bridge housing before leading the way below. At the bottom of the short companionway, Vanessa found herself in a compact and well-lit saloon. Padded seating ran the length of both bulkheads. Behind her to the left lay a small dining area, with the galley on the right.

'He's through there,' advised her guide, indicating a narrow door set into the far bulkhead. 'Only I ought to warn you, he isn't exactly ... I mean ...' He stopped there and sighed again. 'Oh, Lord, you're going to have to know sometime! He passed out last night after drinking most of a bottle of whisky. Lucky he was already lying on the berth because I'd never have got him there without help.'

Vanessa looked at him steadily. 'Does he do it often?'

'Couple of times a month, maybe.' He held her gaze for a bare moment before wryly lifting his shoulders. 'All right then, three or four times. This is the first time he downed a whole bottle though.'

'You mean he usually passes out before he has time to finish it?' she queried drily. 'Where do you fit in?'

'I crew for him. Keep the place ship-shape etcetera.'

'You live on board too?'

'Yes. The name's Brenden, by the way. Brenden Hartley.'

'Vanessa.' She gave him a faint wry smile. 'I think we'd better take a look at him, don't you? We can talk later.'

The for'ard cabin held two berths, the upper one of which was folded back against the bulkhead. The man sprawled across the lower berth was fully dressed in crumpled slacks and shirt, though his shoes had been removed. His features were slack, a two-day stubble covering his jaw in iron grey to match his thinning hair. There was little if any resemblance to the image she had cherished so dearly in her mind's eye these many years.

He stirred restlessly, muttering something un-intelligible without opening his eyes. Vanessa moved forward and picked up the empty bottle from the floor, nostrils pinching as the reek hit her. Seen in close-up he looked even worse, his cheeks sunken beneath sallow skin. She wanted suddenly to weep.

'Let's try and get some coffee down him,' she said. 'Good and black and strong. I could do with some myself, if it comes to that.'

She followed Brenden as he moved back through to the galley, watching his movements as he filled a kettle and set it on the burner. None of this was going the way she had imagined, but she had to make the best of it. One step at a time, that was the only way.

'Have you and my father been together long?' she asked, taking a seat for the simple reason that her legs felt like rubber.

'Six months,' he said. 'It was sheer luck for me that I happened to come along at the right moment. He'd just lost his last mate. The man went back to Tahiti. I knew enough about boats to convince him I could do the job.'

'You haven't always lived on New Caledonia then?'

He laughed. 'Do I sound like it? My French is about on a par with yours.' He paused a moment before adding on a cheerful note, 'I flunked university so I decided to see the world instead. It's five years since I was in England.'

'What about your family?'

'I'm the black sheep—the only one of four brothers to let them down. No ambition, you see. Life's too short to spend the best part of it cooped up in an office somewhere. I started off with a few hundred pounds left me by my grandmother and motorcycled across most of Europe. When that started to run out I found myself a job in Ankara for a couple of weeks—illegally, of course. That's the way I finally got to Australia: a week's work, a week's travel. Not on the bike. I smashed that up in Pakistan. I hitched a couple of rides from there.'

Vanessa laughed, fascinated by the account. 'That has to be the understatement of the year! What made you come to Caledonia?'

'I was making for Fiji, only funds wouldn't stretch.'

'Doesn't my father pay you for doing what you do?'

'Sure he pays me. He makes plenty when . . .'

She finished it for him as he hesitated. 'When he's sober?' They were both silent for a moment or two. Vanessa was the first to speak again. 'Have you any idea how he got started in this line? I don't know all that much about boats, but I'm sure one like this must have cost a bomb.'

'They don't come cheap,' Brenden agreed. 'Especially like the *Julia*. She's equipped with all the latest electronic gear for locating the big game fish. He never has any trouble finding clients.'

He had sidestepped the actual question, whether deliberately or not she wasn't sure. 'He is . . . was an engineer,' she said bemusedly. 'I took it for granted he'd be involved in the mining business here if anything.'

'So he was at one time. It's even said . . .' He broke off abruptly, face flushing a little beneath the tan. 'Just wharfside gossip, that's all. Forget it.'

'Tell me,' she insisted. 'If it has any bearing, I want to hear it.'

His smile was rueful. 'One of these days I'll learn to keep my mouth shut! It's nothing really. Just a rumour that Jules DuTemple put up the money to buy the *Julia* a couple of years ago. I suppose the name doesn't help scotch it.'

'It was my mother's name,' Vanessa said. 'He named it after my mother.'

'Well, there you are then. Just a rumour, the way I said. There's a lot of rivalry when it comes down to netting the tourists. Neal has one of the best equipped boats so he creams off the best deals. It doesn't make him too popular in some quarters.'

It was plausible, but not plausible enough. Rumour, no matter how distorted, had to spring from some basic fact. Yet what was wrong with a loan? 'These DuTemples,' she said slowly. 'They're important people round here?'

'You've said it. One of the biggest of the *"petits mineurs"* if you'll excuse the pun. The company's been in operation since around eighteen-ninety. They sell their ore direct to Japan for processing.' Brenden poured coffee into two mugs and brought one across to where she sat. 'Better drink that before we start trying to get some down your father. He'll be like a bear with a sore head when he does come round.'

Going back to pick up his own mug, he added curiously, 'It must be a long time since you last saw him.'

'It is.' There was no harm, Vanessa decided, in telling him the bare bones of the story. Much of it had to be already obvious anyway.

Brenden heard her out without comment, remaining silent for several seconds after she finished. 'It can't ever be right for a man to do what Neal did,' he acknowledged at last, 'but at the same time I think I have some idea of the way he felt. Some people can't take commitment. Not when it has to be total. Don't hate him for it.'

'I wouldn't be here if I hated him for it,' she pointed out. 'It's all in the past. There's no point.'

'And now you've found him again?'

It was a good question, but not one she was ready to answer. 'It remains to be seen.' She put down the mug and pressed herself to her feet. 'Let's get started.'

It was half an hour or more before Neal Grantham reached the point where he could sit up unaided on the narrow berth. Aching head buried in his hands, he said gruffly, 'Get that girl out of here, Brenden! The last thing I need is any female shoving coffee down my throat!'

'Not just any female,' Vanessa responded, trying to sound matter-of-fact about it. 'I'm your daughter.'

The involuntary jerk of his head brought a groan to his lips. Staring at her out of bloodshot, bleary eyes, he said blankly, 'Good God!'

She had been wrong to spring this on him, Vanessa thought painfully, watching the shame begin to form as realisation struck home. She should have let Brenden bring him round on his own, given him time to assimilate the idea.

'I'll be through in the saloon,' she said. 'We've all the time in the world to talk.'

Brenden followed her. 'He's better left alone to get himself together. A good splash in cold water works wonders.'

Vanessa glanced at him. 'You sound as if you might have been there yourself.'

'Only once.' His grin was sheepish. 'I don't have the stomach for it.'

Nor the need from the sound of it. Vanessa wondered what her father's reasons were.

'Talking of stomachs,' he went on. 'When did you last eat?'

'Breakfast on the plane,' she admitted. Until this moment she hadn't had much time to think about food, but now he came to mention it she could feel the stirring of hunger.

'I make a pretty good omelette,' he offered. 'I'm ready for a bite myself, if it comes to that. Cheese and mushroom okay?'

'Sounds wonderful!' She really meant it. 'Is there anything I can do?'

'No thanks, I'm used to it. Not that we eat here all the time. There's a couple of good little bistros within a stone's throw.'

'Don't you find things a bit cramped actually living on board?' she asked, watching him break eggs into a plastic bowl. 'I mean, it's a super boat, but you must get sick of each other's company at times.'

'I sleep out here,' he said without particular inflection.

It was a moment before she caught his drift, her face faintly flushing. 'I wasn't implying anything like that.'

'Some aren't as charitable. There's no such thing as a simple working relationship these days, it seems.'

'But you still stay.'

'I like the life.'

'It wouldn't be anything to do,' she said softly, 'with the fact that he'd have difficulty finding anyone to take your place, would it?'

Brenden laughed. 'It has something to do with it, sure. I'm no shrinking violet when it comes to taking credit. Labour of any kind is hard to find in these parts. Everybody wants to be their own boss. Any millionaire's wife who wants a house full of servants has to import them.'

'Including the DuTemples?' The question was over-casual.

'There aren't any. Wives, I mean. At least, not right here in N.C. Jules' second wife went on back to the

States when he died last year. Raoul is the last of his line so far. Seems like no woman can come up to his ideals. The mine itself it up north, but the family home is right here in Noumea. There's another house on one of the outer islands, Ile Royale. Privately owned, of course. You need an invitation to go there.'

'You seem to know a lot about the family.'

The glance he gave her was unexpectedly shrewd. 'I could always find out more.'

Vanessa shrugged. 'Just idle curiosity. I met him on the plane from Singapore.'

'Raoul?' He sounded surprised. 'I'd have thought he'd be travelling first-class, if any.'

'And you naturally assume I wouldn't?'

It was Brenden's turn to colour. 'Sorry if I spoke out of turn.'

'You didn't.' She was already ashamed of the caustic retort. 'First-class was apparently overbooked when he checked in. The stewardess actually apologised to him.'

'Daresay she would. He might decide to fly another line next trip.' Brenden leaned over the low dividing unit to slide a plate piled high with fluffy omelette on to the recessed dining table. 'Get it while it's hot. You'll find cutlery in the drawer under there.'

'This is delicious!' Vanessa commented when he joined her a moment later with his own plate. 'I didn't realise how hungry I was.' She glanced towards the inner bulkhead. 'Do you think my father will eat anything?'

'Not for an hour or two. He'll be more dehydrated than anything.'

She dropped her eyes, swallowing on the sudden lump in her throat. 'You're so used to this, aren't you? Was he an alcoholic when you first came to work for him?'

'He isn't an alcoholic. Between times he never touches the stuff.' Brenden paused, shoulders lifting. 'It just seems that every week or so he needs to go on a bender. I suppose it's his way of shutting off.'

From what? Vanessa wondered, forcing herself to carry on eating. What was his connection with the DuTemples? Those were questions only he could answer.

CHAPTER TWO

THEY were still sitting at the table when the inner door opened. Clean shaven, and wearing a fresh shirt and light cotton slacks, the man who stepped through was a vast improvement on that initial sighting, although nothing could disguise the gauntness of his features.

'Is there any more coffee going?' he asked on a low rough note. 'My head feels like it might fall off.' He sat down on the nearest seat as Brenden went to pour a fresh mug, meeting Vanessa's eyes with visible effort. 'Sorry you had to see me that way. It's not how I'd have wanted it.'

It wasn't the way she would have wanted it either, but there was no point in saying it. Her own fault for jumping in without asking first. 'I wrote to you in September,' she said hesitantly, not sure how to ask the question. 'Did you . . .?'

'I got it.' There was apology in the admittance. 'I thought it was better for you if you forgot about me. If you could afford to come out here you must be okay financially.'

'You really believe money is all it takes to make someone happy?' she asked.

He seemed to wince as if from a blow. 'It helps. Without money I wouldn't have the *Julia*. She gave me back my independence.'

'Is that why you named her after my mother?'

'Yes.' His expression softened a little. 'She was a fine woman.'

'Not fine enough to keep you.'

24

The sigh came deep. 'I wasn't cut out for marriage. Not in any circumstances. If I'd stayed I'd have made three people miserable not just one. I realise that's no excuse. I'm not trying to find excuses. What I did I did because I had to—or go mad.'

'I'm not condemning you. I simply couldn't bring myself to leave things the way they were. As a matter of fact, I sold the house to realise the money for this trip. Not that I plan on using it all, of course. It fetched a very good price.'

'It would.' He paused before tagging on slowly, 'So how long do you plan on staying?'

Her chin tilted. 'You'd rather I didn't stay at all?'

'That isn't what I meant. It's just . . .' He broke off, shaking his head. 'I don't think you're going to find a lot here for you, that's all. I can't even offer you room and board.'

'That's all right. There are plenty of hotels in town.' She kept her eyes on his face as she added steadily, 'Raoul DuTemple recommended the Belvedere.'

A muscle jerked suddenly at the side of his mouth as his jaw contracted. 'How the devil . . .'

'They came through from Singapore on the same flight,' Brenden put in, emerging from the galley with the freshly-made coffee. 'Did you want anything to eat, Neal?'

'Not yet.' He had himself under control again, his expression unreadable. 'The Belvedere should be fine, providing you can get a room there. We get tourists all year round on New Caledonia, but the dry season's the most popular. From now to December it's all go.'

'That must be good for business.'

'It is. Means I can afford to pick and choose my customers, for one thing.'

'We need supplies.' Brendon had donned a T-shirt

and a pair of worn espadrilles. 'I'll be back in an hour.'

Vanessa watched him disappear upwards, turning back to find her father watching her.

'Best first mate I've had,' he commented without inflection. 'Looks after me as if I were his own father. Maybe because I accept him for what he is. This is the nearest thing he's had to a home in five years.'

'He told me.' Vanessa sipped at the fresh mug of coffee before adding levelly, 'What happens when he gets restless and moves on again?'

'I'll find a replacement.'

'Will that be easy?'

'I doubt if I'd get the same standard of service.' The tone was dry. 'I don't worry about what might happen. Not anymore.' There was a lengthy pause. When he spoke again it was on a different note. 'What else did DuTemple tell you?'

Vanessa made herself look up. 'We barely spoke. I was asleep most of the flight.'

'But he did say something. That's been obvious from the moment you brought his name up. He knew who you were?'

'Yes.' There was no point in any further prevarication. 'He gave me the impression there was little love lost between the two of you, but he wouldn't tell me why. He said that was up to you.'

'And you think you have a right to know?'

She shook her head. 'Whatever went wrong, it's your own affair.'

'Yes, it is—except you're going to hear a version of it sooner or later, so you may as well start off with the right one.' There was little to be gathered from the worn features. 'The basic facts are that Jules DuTemple provided the finance for me to buy this boat by way of a golden handshake when I resigned from the mining company a couple of years ago to make way for a younger man. I managed the Boulou mine for ten years.'

Vanessa's brow was faintly creased. 'Why should his son object to that?'

'Because Raoul believes I brought some kind of pressure to bear.'

She stared at him. 'You mean . . . *blackmail*?'

'I suppose that's what you'd call it. Apparently he only found out about it after his father died last year.'

'So it was a private gift not a company policy?'

'I suppose it must have been. Jules was a fair-minded man. He obviously saw no reason why I should suffer because certain members of the board wanted me replaced. I'd done a good job over the years. Nobody could deny that. Fifty-four is no age to put a man out to grass!'

Vanessa could agree with that statement. What worried her was the things left unsaid. There were a dozen questions she burned to ask, but no way of doing so without revealing a certain lack of faith in her father's word. Little as she really knew him, she doubted if he were capable of blackmail though. All Raoul DuTemple's suspicions confirmed was that there were skeletons in his own family cupboard which might not stand too much investigation.

'It seems a big change from mining to fishing,' she remarked, shifting away from the subject. 'What made you decide?'

Neal shrugged. 'I'd done a lot of game fishing at the weekends. Enough to get a real feel for it. I'm not saying I'll spend the rest of my life this way, but while ever the customers keep coming I'll keep taking them out. I only need a couple of charters a month to cover overheads, anything above that is a bonus. I sent your mother a cheque last year, there'd have been another this year.'

'Even though you must have realised she never cashed the first one?'

His sallow skin took on a brief tinge of colour. 'All right, so it was a bit late to start making gestures. I'd have done it before if I'd been able to afford it.'

Vanessa wondered fleetingly what kind of salary a mine manager could expect to command in these parts, then dismissed the thought as unworthy of her. 'The investments you left in her name sixteen years ago proved adequate,' she said, forbearing to mention that her mother had taken a job to supplement that income as soon as she, Vanessa, had started school. What difference could it make now? She summoned a smile. 'I have enough in the bank to make life very comfortable, so please don't imagine I came here looking for handouts.'

'No,' he said, 'I don't imagine that. You're not the type.' He studied her a moment, his own smile strained. 'You're very like your mother was at your age. I only hope you don't make the same mistake she did when it comes to finding the right man. Is there anyone?'

'Yes,' Vanessa admitted.

'And he wants to marry you?'

'Yes,' she said again.

'Ah, but you're not sure you want to marry him.' His tone roughened a fraction. 'Then don't do it. Don't do anything you don't feel completely right about. It isn't easy to live with regret.'

It wasn't just his marriage he was talking about, she thought, seeing the look in his eyes. There was something else. It concerned the DuTemples, that much she was sure of. His response to the very name was all the confirmation she needed.

'Did you come straight to New Caledonia after you left England?' she asked, not yet ready to discuss her innermost feelings where Michael was concerned. 'You said you'd been with the Company ten years.'

'I was with the Company almost twelve years altogether. First of all in an advisory capacity, then as manager when the previous one had to retire through ill-health. Raoul wanted the job to go to a Frenchman, but he was only in his twenties then and not powerful enough to carry the board with him. He never forgave me for beating his candidate to it.'

Remembering the way those blue eyes had hardened when Raoul DuTemple had realised who she was, Vanessa could imagine him the kind of man who neither forgave nor forgot very easily. A sudden little shiver ran through her. A goose walking over her grave, her mother would have said. She hoped it wasn't an omen.

Her father was a little more forthcoming when it came down to the earlier years. Two of them, it appeared, had been spent more or less on the move—a few weeks here, a few weeks there. Australia had held him for ten whole months, during which he had worked for a mining company up near Kalgoorlie. It was there that he had first met Jules DuTemple, and received the offer to join the Company. Vanessa made no attempt to press him for more than that bare detail. Some instinct warned her she was better off knowing too little rather than too much.

Brenden returned within the hour looking pleased with himself.

'I booked you a room at the Belvedere,' he announced. 'That means you can relax for the rest of the day. Feeling like lunch yet, Neal? I bought some beef steaks. Thought we might have them grilled with mushrooms and a salad.'

'You can keep the rabbit food,' came the dry reply. 'I'll settle for the steak.'

'Let me do something,' Vanessa offered, getting to her feet. 'At the very least I can make the salad.'

Neal had risen too, not very steadily. 'I'm going up for some air,' he announced. 'Call me when it's ready.'

Brenden laid out the steaks on the grill pan and began seasoning them. 'Don't make me redundant,' he remarked on a light note when his employer had gone. 'I'm not ready to move on yet.'

Vanessa took the huge lettuce and began to peel off the outer leaves. She kept her own tone as light. 'Apart from the fact that I know next to nothing about boats, I doubt if I'll be around long enough for that. He doesn't want me here. I was probably a fool to come at all.'

'But if you hadn't you'd more than likely have spent the rest of your life wondering,' came the shrewd response. 'And don't be too sure about what Neal wants either. He needs someone to care about him. He's needed someone for a long time. What he won't do is admit it.'

She said softly, 'Why does he stay here, Brenden? If the boat is his he could conduct the same business from anywhere in the Pacific.'

'Except that he might not be granted a licence any other place. He relies on tourists for his main trade, which limits the choice in any case. Not that I think he'd consider leaving Caledonia. It's been too long.' He paused, glancing her way with an odd expression in his hazel eyes. 'Don't let him put you off, Vanessa. No matter what he says or doesn't say, I'm sure your coming means a lot to him.'

He was more certain than she was, Vanessa thought wryly, but then he knew her father better than she did. There had never been any particular time-limit set in her mind, so why not simply play it by ear? She had come too far to retreat at the first hurdle.

If she had known nothing about boats and game fishing before, she learned quite a lot during the following week. Reluctant at first to take her out with them when the *Julia* was under charter, Neal relaxed once he realised she was genuinely interested and careful not to get in the way.

The men who hired the *Julia* were highly experienced anglers out to pit their skill against whichever of the larger species they could persuade to take their bait. One of them had taken a four-hundred-pound swordfish the previous year, setting a local record. This year the best he could hook was a blue marlin weighing in the region of two-hundred pounds, which still took five hours to bring in. Watching the man throughout the long fight, feet jammed against the footrest, shoulders straining against the harness, the sweat pouring down his determined features, Vanessa could only feel sorry for the fish. She was astonished, if highly relieved in the end when he ordered it to be cut free.

'It's winning the struggle that really matters,' Brenden explained afterwards. 'A real sportsman doesn't need to take in proof of every catch. After last year he wouldn't be satisfied to show his face with anything under three-hundred anyway. That's the only trouble with setting records. It creates even greater expectations.'

The three of them were eating out as usual in one of the quayside bistros to which Brenden had referred that very first morning. Most of the diners came from the boats, creating a casual atmosphere Vanessa enjoyed. If there was a marring factor at all it was in her father's apparent lack of real communication with the rest of his fellow owners. Greetings were exchanged from time to time, but that was about the extent of it. Not that it seemed to bother him overmuch.

'We don't have much in common,' he had acknowledged the one time she mentioned the subject. 'Most of them have been in this line all their lives. I'm the amateur who beat them at their own game. I don't expect them to like it.' Vanessa could see the point, but after two years she would have expected the resentment to be on the wane. It made her wonder to what extent Raoul DuTemple might have a hand in keeping it alive.

Her own relationship with her father had progressed to a point where they were, outwardly at least, at ease with each other. Brenden himself swore he'd never seen his employer more relaxed.

'We don't have anything scheduled until the middle of next week,' Neal observed now on a casual note. 'Why don't we take a cruise, just the three of us. We could spend a couple of days round the Isle of Pines— maybe even stop in at the Turtle Club on Ouen coming back. Sleeping three on board shouldn't be too difficult if it's organised properly. What do you say?'

Vanessa caught Brenden's eye and knew he was thinking the same thing. Tomorrow was Saturday. Last week at this time her father had already been well down that bottle of Scotch. If her being here prevented even one such repetition then it had been worthwhile coming. She said swiftly, 'That sounds a great idea!'

'Good.' He was smiling himself, fired by her

enthusiasm. 'We'll make an early start. Clear the lagoon before it gets snarled up with weekend traffic.' The smile became a grimace as he reached out a hand for the salt cellar. 'Must have pulled a muscle. This arm of mine aches like hell!'

'There's some linament back on the boat,' said Brenden. 'It might help. Best thing for it is rest. I can do the driving this trip.'

'You'd have us going round in circles.' There was no malice in the retort. 'I'll be okay by morning.'

The two of them walked Vanessa back to her hotel when the meal was over, leaving her as usual at the doors. Crossing the lobby, she thought she saw Raoul DuTemple in the middle of a party just entering the restaurant, but she couldn't be sure. Lean, dark-haired men were not exactly rare in this part of the world. Right or wrong, the very reminder of his existence was enough to take the edge off her day. Even if there should eventually come a time when her father trusted her enough to tell her the whole story, she wasn't sure she wanted to know. It was perhaps better to remain in ignorance.

The following few days were to stay in her memory for a long time to come. They spent two of them on the lovely Isle of Pines, bathing in the blue-green lagoons, shelling on the off-shore islets, barbecueing fish on the beach at sunset. They borrowed scuba gear from the Nauticlub and Brenden taught her the technique. Moving like a fish through the translucent water, Vanessa had never felt so happy and carefree. All thought of Michael and home was pushed to the back of her mind. She had sent a postcard announcing her safe arrival, which was all that was necessary for the moment. Her past life seemed a million miles and almost as many years away.

Neal rose looking tired and a little grey around the mouth on the morning of their departure. Just a touch of indigestion, he claimed when Vanessa expressed some concern. Nothing to get worked up about, Nevertheless, he made no demur when Brenden offered to take them back to Noumea.

He stayed below all morning, refusing to eat any lunch. By mid afternoon he was sweating heavily, feeling nauseous and finding it difficult to breathe due to the growing tightness across his chest. With the nearest hospital in Noumea itself, there was nothing else they could do but carry on making for the mainland at their best speed.

Vanessa stayed with her father throughout the next couple of hours, wringing out towels in cool water to wipe away the sweat from his face and head; trying to ease his discomfort in any way she could. That he was having a coronary there was little doubt. The question was how much worse it was going to get? Her own knowledge of first-aid was hazy to say the least. If only there was oxygen on board!

The weather wasn't helping. Since lunchtime the sun had disappeared behind an ominous bank of cloud building from the west, the sea turned rough. The storm would be on them well before they made land, Brenden acknowledged when Vanessa went to see what was happening up top.

'Our best chance is to put in to Ile Royale,' he shouted above the sound of wave and rising wind. 'We're less than three miles off, and they'll have oxygen.'

Ile Royale. That was Raoul DuTemple's domain. Right now Vanessa would have braved the devil himself to get help for her father.

'So let's do it,' she shouted back.

Neal Grantham's lips were already turning blue, she noted when she got back to his side. She took his hand in hers, trying to warm the chilled flesh, to keep him breathing by sheer force of will. He was dying by inches, right under her eyes, and there was nothing she could do to stop it. Oh, God, she thought, let there be time!

He was still holding on when they reached the island, but only just. Vanessa felt the bump as they came alongside some kind of wharf or jetty, heard voices shouting. Then the hatch was opened and Brenden was coming down the companionway, looking with concern at the man propped up among the berth cushions.

'They're fetching an oxygen tank,' he said. 'He'll need that before we attempt to get him up to the house.'

Neal's eyelids fluttered open. 'What . . . house?' he managed to get out. 'Where . . .?'

Vanessa put her fingers to the blue lips. 'Don't try to talk,' she pleaded. 'Please don't try to talk!'

The effort alone had exhausted his slender reserves. He fought to draw the next breath, face contorted in agony. Feet thudded on the deck above, and suddenly the whole cabin seemed full of people. A mask was fitted over the dying man's face, a valve turned on. For a terrifying moment or two the oxygen seemed to make no appreciable difference. It was only gradually that the rigid limbs began to relax a little, the gaunt face to regain some faint colour. Vanessa allowed herself no more than a passing relief. He wasn't out of danger yet. Not by any means.

'He needs a doctor,' she said to the white-jacketed Asian holding the tank. 'How soon can we get a doctor here?'

The man apparently spoke no English judging from his blank expression. Vanessa repeated the question in hesitant French, thankful to see the blankness lift.

'Two hours, if the weather allows,' he replied in the same language. 'You have radio?'

'It's out.' Brenden met Vanessa's eyes in mute apology. 'It's been out since yesterday afternoon. I was going to fix it when we got back.'

She bit back the hasty exclamation, aware that he could no more have known what was going to happen than she had herself. At least with oxygen her father stood a chance. He would have had none had they tried to make the mainland.

'There is a telephone,' put in the second of the two men, grasping the gist of the conversation. He was also of obvious Asian extraction. 'I will go.'

He was back within ten minutes, accompanied by Raoul DuTemple himself. The latter wasted no time on superfluous questions, ordering his men to form a chairlift for the invalid while Brenden took the weight of the tank in their wake.

The wind had risen several knots, bending the palm trees fringing the white beach as if they were made of straw. More fatigued than she had realised, Vanessa stumbled and would have fallen as she gained the wooden jetty, had Raoul not been there to seize her elbow and pull her upright. For a fleeting second or two she was close up against the lean hard body, aware of his breath on her cheek, the subtle scent of his skin, the sudden flaring sensation in the pit of her stomach. She moved away from him as if stung, jerking her arm from under the long, tapering fingers.

'I can manage, thanks!'

'You came here for help,' he reminded her sardonically. 'At least accept it with good spirit.'

She bit her lip. 'It was the only place we had to go. He couldn't have lasted much longer without oxygen.'

'I agree. And one scuba tank may not be enough. There are others on board the *Etoile*. Wait here.'

The rest of the party was already vanishing into the trees edging the beach, following a path rapidly becoming silted over by the shifting sand. Raoul boarded the cabin cruiser moored on the opposite side of the jetty, reappearing with two more of the small tanks ready strapped into the diving harness.

'These were filled only this morning,' he said, swinging the harness over a shoulder when he was safely back at Vanessa's side. 'We can refill them as many times as needed from the main tank.'

This time when he took her arm she put up no resistance. The wind-driven waves were splashing up between the boards, soaking her to the knees before they reached the landward end of the jetty. Sand clung to her wet jeans, gritting between her teeth and filling her hair. She was thankful to reach the comparative shelter of the trees.

'How will they get out from the mainland in this?' she shouted as Raoul forged ahead to lead the way, but the wind whipped the words from her lips. Glancing back to where the two boats rode at their moorings, she could answer her own question. No one but a fool would risk that sea.

She was too concerned for her father's condition to take in much about the house itself when they reached it, except that it was large and imposing. They crossed a vast hallway tiled underfoot in black and white to mount a curving wrought iron staircase to the galleried upper floor. Brenden met them in the doorway of the room to which they had taken the invalid, his expression was encouraging.

'He seems to be holding his own,' he said. 'Is there anything you need from the boat?'

'Whatever you do need can be supplied,' Raoul assured them both, dumping the tanks inside the door. 'I left instructions for rooms to be prepared.'

Vanessa's eyes were on the bed where her father lay propped up with pillows, the face mask still in place. 'Is there any chance at all of a boat putting out in this?' she asked without much hope.

'I've known Pierre Renaud put out in worse. There's a force nine forecast, so if he's going to get here at all it has to be within the next three hours.' He was looking at Brenden as he spoke. 'I'd have thought a pleasure trip ill-advised considering.'

'The radio's out of action,' admitted the younger man uncomfortably. 'We didn't get the forecast last night, or this morning.'

Dark brows lifted. 'You carry no barometer?'

'Naturally we carry a barometer.' Brenden's face was set, his resentment plain. 'We thought we'd make it back before anything too serious blew up. Neal didn't exactly count on this happening.'

Vanessa moved across to the bed, leaving the two men to it. Her father's eyes were open, his colour vastly improved. His fingers closed about her hand with surprising strength.

'You're going to be all right,' she said softly, reassuring herself as much as him. 'There's a doctor on the way.' She only hoped that was true. 'All you have to do is lie quiet until he gets here. Is the pain still bad?'

The slight negative movement of his head was a comfort in itself. If the pain was passing that surely had to be a good sign. All the same, she was staying with him. He needed her now if he hadn't needed her before.

His breathing had eased considerably by the time they came to change the oxygen bottle. He said no when asked if he wanted more. After that he seemed to drift off to sleep. Left alone with him at her own request, Vanessa began to get cramp sitting upright on the edge of the bed, but she refused to relinquish her father's hand until his fingers relaxed of their own accord.

'You need clean dry clothing,' Raoul observed from the doorway as she stretched her aching limbs, surprising her because she hadn't been aware of his return. 'I've had some of my sister's things left in your room. You look close to the same size.' He caught her swift glance back to the bed, and shook his head. 'He won't be left alone. I'll have Thi-Sen sit with him. She's waiting outside.'

With her sand-heavy jeans still clinging damply to her legs, she could only acknowledge the sense in what he said. She felt bone weary, and not a little weepy. Reaction, she knew. The strain of these past few hours was finally catching up on her.

'Where did Brenden go?' she asked as they moved along the gallery.

'Back to the boat,' Raoul acknowledged. 'He wanted to be sure all was secure.'

'There's a chance of damage?'

'Not so much here. We're protected to a great extent by the curve of the headland.' He paused to open another door, standing back to allow her entry. 'This will be yours as long as you're here on Royale. I'd advise you to try and get some sleep.'

'I couldn't,' she protested. 'My father—he might need me.'

'If he did you'd be called.' He looked at her critically. 'You'll be doing him little good by collapsing from exhaustion yourself. Take a warm shower and at least lie down for a while.'

The room was pleasantly dim, its windows shuttered against the elements. Thick deep carpeting gave underfoot. Too tired to take in more than the bare details of the tastefully luxurious furnishings, Vanessa moved on through to the superbly appointed bathroom and stripped off her soiled garments. The warm water did little to revive her. She felt weighed down by depression. Blaming herself for what had happened was ridiculous, and she knew it, yet the shock of having her turn up out of the blue the way she had might well have contributed to the attack. One thing was certain, if her father lived she wouldn't be leaving him again. She'd find a job out here; make her home out here. Michael would understand—he would have to understand. She wouldn't have made him a very good wife anyway.

CHAPTER THREE

SHE awoke disorientated, eyes going blankly around the unfamiliar room then down to the pale silk pegnoir covering her body.

Memory returned with heart-jerking suddenness, bringing her upright on the bed. She could hear the lash of rain against the closed shutters, see the flicker of lightning through the cracks, yet it was surely only a moment or two ago since she had closed her eyes.

It was necessary to switch on one of the bedside lamps in order to see the time by her watch. Six o'clock already! How could it be? She had only intended to rest for a few minutes.

Everything must be all right, she told herself reassuringly, or they would surely have called her. She clung to that thought as she exchanged the robe for the garments laid out ready over a chair. Even at a time like this she could appreciate the feel of silk next to her skin, the excellent cut and fit of the pale blue slacks and shirt. The matching mules were a little tight across the arch of her foot, but it was needs must. Her own canvas casuals were hardly in any fit state to wear.

Raoul was a good judge: she and his sister were similar in both height and build. Brenden had said nothing about a sister that first morning, but then why should he have? Her interest had been in Raoul himself—in his connection with her father. Considering the enmity existing between the two men, she had to be doubly grateful for his help now.

Brenden was outside when she opened the door, his hand lifted, ready to knock.

'I brought your clothes up from the boat,' he said, holding out a rolled bundle. 'I thought you'd probably prefer your own things to someone else's.'

'I would have done,' Vanessa acknowledged, taking them from him. 'Only now I'm dressed I may as well stay the way I am. How's my father?'

'You'll have to ask his physician.'

'He got here!' Relief flooded her. 'When?'

'Half an hour ago. Just before the rain started. It's going to get worse before it gets better, as they say, so I'm afraid we're all stuck here for the duration.'

'No damage to the boat?'

'Not so far, though she's certainly taking a battering. So is the *Etoile*, if it comes to that. Not that our host seems to be overly concerned. What's a boat or two to a man worth his kind of money!'

Vanessa dropped the bundle of clothing in the nearest chair and came out on to the gallery to join him. 'He certainly got across you, didn't he,' she remarked. 'You know, he did have a point.'

'Think I don't appreciate it?' The tone was wry. 'It's that superior attitude of his that rankles. The sooner we're out of this place the better!'

'That will have to depend on when Dad is going to be fit to be moved. Having come this far, I doubt if Raoul is going to throw us all out as soon as the storm moves off.'

'Raoul now, is it?'

Vanessa glanced at him swiftly, sensing the barb behind the comment. 'You think it would be presumptuous of me to call him that to his face?'

Brenden flushed. 'Neal's hardly going to like it if you get too friendly with him.'

'He's hardly in any position it complain no matter what.' Vanessa paused, giving vent to a sudden sigh. 'Look, Bren, I don't want to quarrel with you. Dad owes you a lot. As to getting too friendly with Raoul DuTemple—well, it's hardly likely, is it? I'm sure he's as eager to have us all off the island as you are to leave it.'

They had reached the door of her father's room. The small dark-haired man with the stethoscope round his neck looked up at their entry, his gesture bidding them to be quiet. Neal lay propped up on several pillows, his eyes closed. The blue tinge had gone from his lips, Vanessa was thankful to note.

'He is under sedation,' Doctor Renaud said softly, drawing her away from the bed. 'It will be several hours before he wakens.'

'How is he?' Vanessa asked, adopting the same quiet tone. 'Is he going to recover?'

The doctor studied her face for a brief moment before replying. 'Your father's condition appears stabilised now, so it would be advisable for him to stay where he is for the present. Perhaps in a week or so, providing nothing else occurs, we can think about getting him back to the mainland for more extensive tests.'

'Does that mean he has a chance?'

'It means he has every chance. The first few hours are the crucial ones.'

She searched the thin features, hoping he was telling her the whole truth. 'And the future?'

'Providing he takes things in moderation, he could make a complete recovery. Persuading him to sell that boat of his might be an advisable step. Do you intend staying in New Caledonia yourself?'

Her mind was already leaping ahead, calculating

the possibilities. With what the boat should bring plus the sum she could have transferred here from England, there should be enough to set the two of them up in a modest home and provide the necessities. Her secretarial qualifications were surely good enough to secure her a job, although she would have to brush up on her French. There were such things as work permits too. That might prove more difficult. She was going to need help, and there was only one person she knew who was likely to hold the necessary sway. Whether he would be prepared to offer his aid under the circumstances was something else again. There was only one way she was going to find out, and no point in delaying the moment.

'Yes,' she said, 'I'm staying. Do you know where I might find *Monsieur* DuTemple?'

'He said he would be in the library if needed. I will show you.' His glance moved to Brenden still standing over by the door. 'Perhaps you will sit with our patient while I get some food? I haven't eaten since mid-morning.'

Until that moment Vanessa had completely forgotten the younger man's presence. If the *Julia* was sold he was going to be out of a job, unless the new owner was willing to keep him on as crew. She couldn't afford to worry too much about that aspect anyway. Her father's health had to be her main concern.

Dr Renaud accompanied her down the lovely staircase, pausing to point out the double, mahogany doors to the library before continuing on his way to other quarters. Vanessa tapped lightly on the wood and was invited to enter, finding Raoul standing before one of the tall wall shelves with a leather-bound volume open in his hand as if he had been checking some fact. White cotton pants fitted closely about his lean hips, cinched at the waist by a soft leather belt. His black shirt was opened halfway down the front, revealing a glimpse of dark body hair and the glint of gold at his throat.

'Come in,' he repeated as she hesitated on the threshold. Closing the book, he slid it back on to the shelf. 'You've seen your father?'

'And Dr Renaud,' she acknowledged, obeying the injunction. 'I'm more than grateful to him for making the trip in this weather.'

'He's a dedicated man. If there's any chance at all of reaching a patient he'll take it, even if it means putting his own life at risk.'

'Is that what he did today?'

In here, as in the rest of the house, the storm shutters were closed against the raging elements, the lamps lit. It scarcely needed the faint lift of his eyebrow to underline his response to the question.

'It's called talking for the sake of talking,' Vanessa admitted ruefully. 'I'd have felt so dreadfully responsible if anything had happened to him. I hardly know how to thank you for taking us in.'

'You thought I might be capable of turning you away?'

Green eyes met blue, refusing to flinch from the encounter. 'Your feelings for my father aren't exactly friendly.'

'Hardly relevant when a man is on the verge of dying.'

'I'm told he's out of immediate danger now.' She nerved herself to go on. 'I need to know exactly what it is you have against him. Can we discuss it?'

His regard was disquieting. 'Is this the time?'

'Waiting won't make it any easier.'

'Quite true.' He shrugged suddenly, and indicated

one of the comfortably deep leather chairs. 'Sit down and tell me what you already know.'

Vanessa made herself move to take the nearest of the chairs, sitting upright on the edge of it with her hands curving the arm ends. She could see the tension whitening the back of her knuckles. How did she start?

'I've been told you're under the impression he had some kind of hold over your father,' she said at length.

Raoul had remained standing. His expression now gave nothing away. 'And . . .?'

She gazed at him helplessly. 'What possible pressure could he have brought to bear on a man of your father's standing? Isn't it more feasible to suppose that having brought him here to New Caledonia in the first place, your father felt moved to make some form of reparation when he was kicked out to make way for a younger man? At fifty-four the chances of his finding another job had to be limited.'

'In this part of the world his chances were nil.' Raoul's tone was quite level, his stance unaltered. 'So he has you believing in his innocence.'

'He's my father. Of course I believe him.'

The smile held no trace of humour. 'You met him again little more than a week ago after sixteen years. I was never more than a few months away from my own father, yet he wasn't the man I always believed he was.'

Vanessa's head went back. 'You mean he had something to hide?'

'If he hadn't there would have been no problem.' He watched the doubt beginning to creep into her eyes, his own unrelenting. 'The DuTemples have business interests outside of New Caledonia itself. My father commuted regularly to the Australian mainland. Some years ago your father was working for a mining company near Kalgoorlie. The two of them were briefly introduced at some local social function or other. Less than a year later, after losing his job at the Landarra mine, your father came here to Caledonia looking for work. One of those quirks of fate no one can foresee. He saw a photograph of my father in a newspaper, along with his wife—my stepmother. Recognition was apparently instant. He took full advantage of what he knew.'

Vanessa looked her bewilderment. 'You're saying he cajoled your father into giving him a job on the strength of that former meeting? On what gounds?'

'On the gounds that in Kalgoorlie both the name and the wife had been different.' Raoul was speaking quietly enough but with an underlying rawness to his voice. 'A few discreet inquiries revealed the truth. My father had spent fifteen years of his life hiding a second family. There were two children, both boys. The one redeeming factor was the lack of a bigamous ceremony.'

It was a moment or two before Vanessa could bring herself to make any comment. 'How did you find out about all this?' she managed at length.

'He left me a personal letter along with the will when he died last year. In it he confessed everything.'

'And accused my father?'

'Yes. It explained so many things that had puzzled me over the years.' The firm mouth twisted. 'Obviously I could bring no charges without revealing the motive, which I wasn't willing to make public property. Your father knew that. Perhaps it was guilt that started him drinking in the first place, but it didn't stop him from driving that final bargain when even my father's power proved unequal to the task of convincing the board that he could still cope with his job. With a boat like the *Julia* he could be financially independent. True, he kept his word after that, and never came back for more, but that's no mitigation. He'd already ruined my father's health.'

'There was some contribution on his own part,' she protested numbly. 'You can't condone what he did.'

Raoul shrugged. 'I can understand a man taking a mistress in certain circumstances. What I can't condone is the fact that he had children by her.' The pause held deliberation. 'What are your own plans for the future?'

Vanessa said thickly, 'I'm staying with him. He's going to need me.'

'You don't care what he did?'

'Yes, I care. I have to care. But he's still my father.'

It was a moment or two before he spoke again. The eyes resting on her face were enigmatic. 'The choice is yours,' he said at length. 'You realise it will be several days before he can safely be moved?'

'That's what Dr Renaud said.' She hesitated, wishing there were some other way. 'Brenden will naturally go over to the mainland as soon as the storm's over and start making the necessary arrangements.' She was coming to her feet as she spoke. 'In the meantime . . .'

'In the meantime,' he interrupted smoothly, 'we'll put the whole affair aside. You were right, what's done is done. There's no point now in dwelling on it.'

Was that what she had implied? It sounded so callous. Yet there was no other course to take. Whatever her father had been in the past it was here and now that had to matter most. One way in which they could make some small amends was by returning whatever price the *Julia* fetched to its rightful owner. Raoul hardly needed the money but he might appreciate the principle. Providing she could get everything else transferred out here without too much trouble, they would manage.

Raoul moved to press a bell-push set into the wall. 'You must be hungry,' he said. 'Dinner is usually served at nine, but I can have it brought forward.'

'Not for me, please,' she protested. 'I really don't feel like eating.'

'Some hot tea then? Not the kind of stimulant I relish myself, but the household staff set great store by it.'

'Are they all Asian?'

'Vietnamese, to be exact. The original family settled here in Ile Royale after World War Two. Since then, of course, they've been joined by others. They have their own small township close by. Few consider leaving for any length of time. They count themselves fortunate.'

'I'm sure they do.' They were making conversation, Vanessa acknowledged ruefully, but it was better than nothing. 'Vietnam itself is no place to be these days, is it? We have some boat people in England.'

'They must have had a hard time adjusting to your weather.' He looked round as the door opened to admit a slight young woman wearing a cool white linen dress, switching to French. 'Would you bring tea for one, please, Lan.'

The girl inclined her smooth dark head without speaking, and disappeared as softly and silently as she had come. Vanessa wondered who else knew the story Raoul had just told her. Not that she imagined he would have made free with the details himself, but these things had a way of getting round. As Brenden had said, the sooner they could leave the island the better it was going to be for everyone. Even now she was still so vitally aware of Raoul as a man. If only things could have been different.

And what if they had been? asked the voice of common sense. She would still have been outside that rarefied world in which he moved.

'I must thank your sister for the loan of her things,' she said, trying to keep a level head. 'Is she here?'

'Not at the present time. She's visiting her mother in New York.'

'Then she's only your half sister?'

'Not even that. My mother died when I was born. Father waited fifteen years before he married again—a widow with the one child. Crystal is twenty-five now.'

'It's an unusual name.'

'It suits her.' He paused. 'Won't you sit down again. If we're going to be several days in the same house it would be as well to make them as relaxed as possible.'

'We could keep out of each other's way,' she suggested, complying. 'I understand the way you must feel.'

His smile was faint. 'The way I feel is that there is nothing to be gained from our becoming enemies. You're going to need help if you stay in Caledonia. I can supply it.'

'Why should you?'

'Perhaps because I have a weakness for luminous green eyes.' The smile grew as her expression altered. 'You expect me to believe you weren't aware of the attraction you have for me when you came down here to plead for your father?'

'I didn't come to plead,' she protested. 'Only to find out the truth.'

'Before asking my help?'

'Well, yes, I suppose so. Only it seemed a waste of time once I knew how things were.'

'We already agreed to put the past aside.'

'But not to forget it altogether.'

'Only time can bring forgetfulness. In the meantime life must go on.'

The opening of the door curbed any reply she might have made. Raoul waited until the tray had been deposited on one of the low tables before saying calmly, 'There are one or two matters I have to attend to. Enjoy your tea. I'll see you at dinner.'

Left alone, Vanessa stood for a moment or two trying to collect herself. He could have been mocking her, but somehow she doubted it. If he had been mocking anyone it had been himself. Life must go on, yes, but it wasn't going to be simple. The way she was beginning to feel about Raoul was too tangible an emotion to be ignored.

The storm blew itself out in the early hours. By sunrise the sky was clear again, the sea already settling to its normal limpid swell. Dr Renaud left for the mainland before breakfast, having first assured himself that his patient remained in a stable condition.

'Try to keep his mind at rest, if you can,' was his parting advice to Vanessa. 'Mental strain of any kind is the last thing he needs. I'll be back in two days to check on his progress.'

'If he's to be stopped from worrying about things you can hardly start asking him to put the *Julia* up for sale,' Brenden pointed out later when she accompanied him down to the jetty to see him off. 'As I told you last night, I can cope on my own for as long as necessary. Maybe later, when he's stronger, there won't be any need to sell. The two of you can still live ashore.'

Without actually stating her reasons, it was

impossible to make him understand. Not that it made any difference, Vanessa was forced to concede. He was right. Everything had to wait until her father regained his strength.

'Don't forget to bring some more of my things from the mainland out tomorrow,' she said. 'I can't keep on borrowing.'

'I'll be here,' he promised. His smile was reassuring. 'Don't worry, it's going to be all right. Neal's tough.'

The boat was a speck on the horizon before she could bring herself to turn away shorewards again. The once unsullied white beach was littered with debris, the trails of seaweed already beginning to smell as they dried in the heat of the sun. Broken palm fronds lay everywhere.

Raoul emerged from the trees before she reached them, waiting for her to come to him.

'You were gone so long OI thought you'd decided to sail too,' he said. 'Your father is awake and asking for you.'

She gave him a swift sideways glance as he fell into step beside her, conscious of his lean vitality in the faded denim jeans and close-fitting T-shirt. 'You've seen him?'

'No. I think it will be better if I stay away from him until he's on his feet again and better able to cope. He isn't going to find it easy to accept my hospitality.'

Vanessa could imagine. She wasn't finding it all that easy herself. 'Why do you carry on living here now you're on your own?' she asked, anxious to change the subject. 'I'd have thought the mainland so much more convenient.'

'I have a home there too,' he admitted. 'Mainly for business and entertaining purposes. I come here to Royale to get away from it all for a while. Don't you ever feel that kind of need?'

'I don't suffer the same pressures.' She waited a moment before adding ruefully, 'I only wish there'd been some other choice—especially knowing what I know now. You really got stuck with us.'

'I could always move back to Noumea if I found the situation untenable,' he replied lightly enough. 'I have to visit the mine within the next day or two, in any case.'

'You'll be leaving?' Her reaction was too strong and she knew it; she made haste to temper it. 'I'm going to feel we've driven you from your own home!'

'Hardly that. As I said, it's a trip I have to make. You'll still be here when I get back.'

It was almost a promise. Vanessa wished she could make herself believe he meant it as such. Yet what could she hope from him? He had said she attracted him, nothing more. Even had circumstances been different their relationship could at best have been a fleeting one. In fact, if circumstances *had* been different he would probably have forgotten her within minutes of stepping off the plane last week.

There was time and opportunity to view the house in more detail this morning. Tall and white, it had a roof of weathered red tiles and a balconied upper floor supported by climber-clad pillars. The lawns fronting it were extensive and well-kept, their emerald reaches already swept clear of storm debris. The two men who yesterday had greeted the *Julia*'s arrival were hard at work tidying the dashed and flattened flower beds.

'I don't blame you for wanting to spend time here,' Vanessa commented impulsively as they made their way indoors. 'It's beautiful!'

'My grandfather built the house over eighty years ago,' Raoul acknowledged. 'Not with his own two hands, of course. Every piece of stone had to be shipped out, so it took a long time.'

'But worth the effort in the end.'

'Not everyone would agree with you. My stepmother had no feeling for the place—or for *Calédonie* itself, for that matter.'

He had spoken without particular inflection. Vanessa said softly, 'I suppose she felt there was nothing to hold her here once your father had gone.'

'It was only money that held her here when he was alive,' came the sardonic response. 'Fortunately he realised it and made sure the properties came directly to me. Otherwise they'd have been sold. Naturally, she was amply compensated, and only too delighted to return home to America on a permanent basis.'

'But her daughter stayed.'

His tone altered subtly. 'Crystal was old enough to make the choice for herself. She managed to do it without making an enemy of her mother.' They had come to a halt opposite the library doors. The blue gaze rested on Vanessa's face, penetrating her defences while giving away nothing of himself. 'Perhaps later, when your father is resting, you might like to take a swim? The reef surrounding Ile Royale isn't high enough in most places to keep out the more dangerous species, so one of the small coves is secured by a shark net stretched across the entrance. It takes no more than a few minutes to walk there from the far end of the rear terrace. You can't get lost.'

She had thought for a moment that he had meant to accompany her. She wasn't sure now whether to be relieved or sorry. 'Thanks,' she said. 'I probably shall.'

He went on into the library as she walked away, closing the door behind him. Vanessa ran lightly up the stairs and found her father's room, thanking the wrinkled old woman who had been sitting with him.

'I don't need someone with me all the time,' Neal protested weakly from among the supporting pillows. 'There's a bell right here beside me.' His eyes sought hers, revealing strain. 'He's told you, hasn't he?'

Prevarication was a waste of time and effort. He had to know sometime. 'He's told me,' she said. 'But only because I insisted on it.'

'So you never really believed my version in the first place.' He sounded wry. 'I can't blame you for that.'

Vanessa sat down on the edge of the bed and took his thin hand in hers. 'It doesn't matter now,' she said. 'It's all in the past. Raoul is prepared to forgive and forget, so you have to put it aside too.'

There was no relief in the drawn features. 'He might have told you that but don't put any trust in it. He swore revenge a year ago when he first found out what I'd done. Somehow or other he'll make me pay.'

'That was a year ago. If he'd been going to take any action at all he'd have done it before this. What could he do anyway?'

'I don't know. All I do know is what he said that day he came to see me. He wouldn't even let me try to explain the way it all happened.'

Vanessa said softly, 'How *did* it happen?'

'It wasn't planned. Not in the same sense.' He paused, looking at her with a kind of desperation. 'When I went to see Jules DuTemple I had no real intention of forcing him into giving me a job. If he'd said no that would have been it. I'd have kept my mouth shut.'

'But he didn't say no?'

'He didn't say anything very much, just told me I was on the payroll as of that date. If I committed any crime at all it was in letting him take certain things for granted.'

He believed it himself, that was obvious. Vanessa scarcely knew what to think. It seemed such an unlikely tale on the face of it, yet she had never known Jules DuTemple personally so how could she guess his probable reactions? Not that it provided any real excuse for her father, in any case. Deep down he must be aware of that.

'You have to put it behind you,' she said. 'Start again. I'm not going back to England. I'm staying right here in Caledonia with you—or any place else you might want to go. Brenden is going to run the *Julia* for the time being. He's confident he can handle it.'

The smile came reluctantly. 'More than I am. Still, if I survive the next couple of weeks it shouldn't be so long before I can take over again myself.'

It was too soon to start talking about selling the boat. Vanessa contented herself with a smile and a nod. 'You've years ahead of you yet.'

CHAPTER FOUR

HE fell asleep again after that, sedated by the tablets Dr Renaud had left. Watching the drained face, Vanessa wondered if there would ever come a time when she would feel really close to this man who was her father only in name still at present. He had made no comment regarding her professed intention to stay. She couldn't be sure he even wanted her to stay. Perhaps she should wait a while before committing herself, she thought disconsolately.

The sunlight filtering in through the slatted window screens was a temptation. There was little she could do while the patient slept except sit and twiddle her thumbs, yet to simply leave him lying here alone seemed so heartless. Supposing he had another attack and failed to reach the bell to summon aid?

As if in answer to her thoughts, the door behind her opened to admit the same wizened old woman who had been here on her arrival. The latter didn't speak at all, just came over to the bed and took the chair she had occupied before, eyes fixed on the sleeping man's face.

Acting under orders, Vanessa surmised. She looked capable enough despite her age. It was pointless the two of them sitting there together. She could always come back later.

Along in her own room, she fished out a turquoise cotton bikini and got into it, slipping on a short towelling jacket, which would double as a towel. The air outside was still fresh after the storm. It felt good on her bare legs. Standing on the covered terrace, she looked out over more lawns and ruined flower beds to the palm plantations no longer cultivated for gain. There was higher ground towards the centre of the island, green and verdant beneath the clean blue sky. Nice, Vanessa thought, then laughed out loud at the understatement. Dreamy would be a more apt expression.

She found the path Raoul had indicated without difficulty, winding down through the trees to come out on a tiny cove so exquisite it caught the breath. Protected as it was it had escaped storm damage almost entirely. Apart from the lapping of waves breaking gently over the silver crescent of sand, and the rhythmical, ever-present humming of the cicadas, there was no sound. Two rocky arms of land curved inwards to within a hundred feet or so. The line of buoys stretched across the gap were the only marring feature of the whole scene. The shark net, of course. Even Paradise had its drawbacks.

Slipping out of the jacket, Vanessa dropped it on the sand and ran into the water. The initial plunge in the sun-warmed temperature was delicious. Within feet of the shore, the sandy bottom shelved steeply. She followed it down, enchanted with the clarity of vision. Fish abounded, shading every colour under the sun as they scattered lazily before her, none of them more than a few inches in length. It was like being inside a huge aquarium.

The net was made of steel wire, anchored at each end and along the bottom by great pins driven into rock and sand. Vanessa went close to look through to deeper water where life was on a larger scale yet scarcely less prolific. Visibility was limited by distance, shading off into darkness. Diving a second time, she thought she caught a glimpse of something big moving out there, but it was too fleeting an impression to be sure. This side of the net there was nothing to worry about anyway.

A sudden shift in pressure drew her head sharply round, although her fingers continued to cling to the steel netting. Raoul arrived in a flurry of bubbles, the jerk of his head ordering her to the surface. They came up within a couple of feet of each other, treading water to keep themselves upright.

'I could see you hanging there,' he said. 'I thought you were caught up on the wire! Didn't you hear me call before you dived again?'

'If I had, I'd have waited,' she came back on a reasonable note. 'I didn't even realise you were in the water.'

'What were you looking for?'

'Sharks,' she admitted, and saw his smile form reluctantly.

'You could wait a long time for that. The net is there as a precaution only, not because the sea teems with the creatures.' He glanced towards the shelf of rocks a few yards away. 'Come and rest for a moment before we swim back to the beach.'

Vanessa didn't need to be told she had overdone it; her muscles were already doing that for her. She had been in the water more than half an hour without taking a breather. The rock extended below the surface in a series of steps, making it possible to climb to a seat on the jutting ledge. Raoul followed her, perching close enough for her to feel the touch of his bare thigh against hers. Moving away would serve only to underline the effect that contact was having on her so she let it lie, lifting her hands to sleek the water from her hair.

Raoul leaned forward a little to rub the side of his foot where it had scraped on the rock, revealing the tanned breadth of his back. His skin was smooth, the muscles of his shoulders and upper arms well-developed. Vanessa knew a sudden urgent desire to put out a hand and run her fingers lightly down the line of his spinal column—to feel his body tense the way hers was tensed. She wasn't innocent enough to suppose that his joining her had been any sudden whim on his part. The suggestion that she swim here this morning had been made with purpose.

'You're quivering.' He said it without turning his head. 'I can feel your skin fluttering. Not cold, I hope?'

'Not at all,' she said on as level a note as she could manage. 'You must be well accustomed to having women tremble to your touch!'

He sat back again to look at her, eyes too knowledgeable by half. 'Are you mocking me or defending yourself?'

'What difference does it make?'

'Very little.' He put out a hand and turned her face towards him, his palm cupping the side of her jaw. 'I was drawn to you from the very first moment I saw you on the plane at Singapore. Discovering who you were altered the situation, I admit, but we were obviously meant to come together again.'

'My father . . .' she began.

'Is another matter altogether. I can't take revenge on a sick man.'

She searched the blue eyes, trying to penetrate the depths. 'You really mean that?'

'I really mean it.' He was smiling, the ball of his thumb softly caressing her skin. 'You're not like others I've known, Vanessa. You would have had adequate reason to turn round and go home again the moment you discovered what kind of man your father had become, but you stood by him. You could even find it in you to defend what he did.'

Her senses were alive to that slow, stroking movement. 'Not defend,' she murmured, 'just try to understand. It wasn't planned, Raoul. He swears he never really intended to threaten your father with exposure. All he wanted was a job.'

Something flickered deep down in his eyes but the smile remained. 'We agreed to put all that aside, remember? This is between the two of us, no one else.'

His lips were cool and tasted of salt. She felt the tremors start deep down inside her at the first questioning touch of his tongue, the sudden pressure as her thighs went into spasm. She answered in kind, becoming ever more sensually aroused as he probed deeper and more intimately, her hands slid up behind his head to hold him closer. It wasn't the first time she had been kissed this way, but never before had she been stirred to respond with such eager abandon— made so totally and vibrantly aware of her body's needs. She wanted to be part of this man, to feel him moving inside her, assuaging the ache that threatened to engulf her.

Too fast, a part of her mind remained sane enough to tell her. It was happening too fast. She drew away from him abruptly, closing her eyes as she leaned her head back against the rock face to regain her breath. Raoul made no attempt to take hold of her again. An age seemed to pass before he spoke, his voice so soft it was almost a caress in itself:

'Come back to the beach. No one will disturb us.'

He had probably made sure of that, she thought with swift cynicism. She made herself open her eyes and look at him, sufficiently in command again to meet the vivid gaze without flinching. 'I have to get back to my father.'

'Your father is in good hands. There's nothing for you to do.' He was still speaking softly, expression devoid of mockery. 'Would you deny what was there in you a moment ago?'

'Would you deny that you followed me down here with the intention of making love to me?' she flashed in response, and saw his head incline.

'Why should I lie? I'm as much aware of the attraction we have for each other as you are yourself.'

The shake of her head repudiated that statement. 'I'm not even your type!'

'And what would you consider my type?'

'Beautiful, sophisticated, used to your kind of world. I'm none of those things.'

'True,' he agreed. 'There was even a time when you would have been right, except that I'm no longer at an age where surface impressions mean the most. There's no shortage of the kind of woman you describe in this part of the world, believe me. Sometimes I'm tempted to suspect many of them may be cloned. You're fresh and original, Vanessa. You allow your emotions to show.'

She said wryly, 'I'll have to practise self-control a little more.'

His gaze dropped to the curve of her breasts clearly outlined beneath the clinging material covering them. 'Some responses are difficult to conceal,' he observed. 'Especially when wearing so little. We react in similar fashion to certain stimulation—male or female. Failing a cold shower, a vigorous swim comes recommended.'

He was taunting her now, though not unkindly. Vanessa slid into the water and struck out for the beach, resisting the impulse to go for speed. Raoul was a powerful swimmer; he might just misconstrue the gesture as a challenge. She couldn't doubt that he wanted her; he had deliberately drawn her attention to the fact. What she still doubted was his motivation. She was the daughter of the man on whom he had sworn revenge. He couldn't have forgotten that. Not completely. Yet taking her wasn't going to make her father suffer. Not unless he planned on flaunting the fact in front of a sick man. She didn't want to believe him capable of such cold-hearted calculation.

He was right behind her when she emerged from the water, catching her up to swing her round into his arms. Standing there with the waves swirling about their ankles, she tried to avoid his mouth, desisting only when he pulled her up close against him. The hardness of his body sent hot shivers racing through her, blanking off thought in an onslaught of sensation. Instictively she moulded to the shape of him, kissing him back with a kind of resignation; feeling his thigh muscles tense, her senses beginning to fuse.

The touch of his fingers at her centre back was so gentle she scarcely knew what he was doing until her bikini top slid away from between their bodies, baring her firm uptilted breasts to an electrifying contact with crisp, curling hair. Her nipples felt as if on fire, the pressure almost unbearable. She eased herself slightly away from him, providing the room for his hands to explore, a tiny moan breaking from her lips as the long fingers curved about her. If there had ever been a time for drawing back it was past and gone. She had come too far to want to draw back.

One arm slid about his neck when he bent and scooped her bodily up out of the water, her back arching to bring her breasts closer to the seeking lips.

His tongue was both torture and delight, tracing a spiral which ended at her nipple, flickering over the tender tip until every nerve in her was stretched to breaking point. Then he was lifting his head to look into her eyes, his own so vividly, passionately fired she couldn't look away.

'Not here,' he said softly. 'I know a better place.'

Vanessa clung to him as he carried her up the sand, hardly caring where they went. Just within the trees, and blended into them, stood a small palm-thatched hut. A single unglazed window opening provided a diffused light. Raoul set her down on the rush-matted floor and began to kiss her again, his fingers pulling open the side-tie strings of her bikini bottom to let it drop from her.

The sensation of being nude in his arms was exquisite. When he pressed her down on her back to the floor where he could see her in detail she felt no reticence, only delight that her body could bring that look to his eyes. She watched him straighten to remove his trunks, pulses racing to the sight of him. Michael's lovemaking had been pleasant, even stirring at times, but never like this. But she couldn't think about Michael now. She didn't want to think about anything or anyone except this man and this moment. It was too late to start having doubts. Far, far too late.

Nevertheless, she stiffened a little as Raoul's weight came down over her. Sensing it, he lifted himself slightly away on his bent elbows, dropping his head to find her mouth in a kiss that drove all other concerns from her mind. His lips moved along the line of her jaw to her ear, creating a wholly new kind of tension as his murmuring voice described what he was going to do to her, told her what he wanted from her. By the time he parted her thighs she was at fever pitch, limbs wrapping about him as he came into her, body moving in response to that thrusting, demanding force until everything dissolved into the one glorious explosion.

It took the touch of Raoul's lips against her closed lids to make her open her eyes. He was smiling as he watched her, registering the satiated glaze. 'It was good for you?' he asked, already knowing the answer.

Vanessa put out the tip of her tongue and ran it over dry lips, seeing his gaze suddenly kindled again. 'That has to be what one would call a purely rhetorical question,' she murmured. 'You made sure it was.' The expertise, came the reluctant thought, of experience.

'What is it?' He had seen her expression alter, her mouth faintly compress. 'What are you thinking?'

She moved her head on the mat in negative response. 'Nothing important.'

'If it could cause that look to pass across your face then it has to be important,' Raoul insisted. 'Tell me.'

'All right.' Her tone was just slightly defensive. 'I was wondering how many others have been in this same position with you before me. Idle curiosity, that's all.'

'Far from idle, I think.' The smile had vanished. 'It's a question most women ask sooner or later. Why should I have expected any different from you?'

'I don't expect an answer,' she denied swiftly. 'I don't even really want to know.'

'That's good, because I have no intention of telling you.' He rolled away from her to reach for the discarded trunks, pulling them on as far as his thighs before kneeling to tug them up over his hips. 'I'll fetch you your bikini top if you wait here,' he added, getting to his feet.

She had tied the strings at her hips when he returned. Taking the slip of material from him, she put it on and fastened it before looking up to meet his eyes, self-conscious in his presence.

'I ruined everything, didn't I?' she said miserably. 'I shouldn't have told you.'

He shrugged. 'I shouldn't have asked. We're all of us entitled to think our own thoughts.' He paused, studying her a moment, then reached out a hand to touch her cheek. 'We start again, yes? No past, only the present.'

And probably little future, came the fleeting reflection, but this time she kept the doubt to herself. Raoul was making no promises, offering no incentives. If she went along with what he was saying she ran the risk of falling in love with a man who would never return the emotion. Even if by chance she was wrong about that, there was still the question of her father. Sick or not, he was a constant reminder of that past Raoul was attempting to put aside.

None of it reckoned in the end because she couldn't bring herself to walk away from the affair. Making love with Raoul was an experience she wanted to repeat—had to repeat. Right now would not be too soon.

He saw the look in her eyes and laughed softly, leaning forward to press a fleeting kiss on her lips. Vanessa stopped herself from clinging to him when he drew away from her again, aware of the message. He was in control, and intended to stay that way.

'You wouldn't want to miss your lunch,' he said. 'Tonight we'll have time and to spare.'

A tremor ran through her. 'Tonight?'

'Of course.' His smile came slow. 'You didn't seriously believe you were going to spend it alone after this? We only just began learning about each other.'

'My father,' she ventured. 'The servants . . .'

'They know better than to pass on anything they either see or hear to anyone.' He took her by the shoulders, making her look at him. 'You're an adult, not a child. You don't need your father's approval to form a liaison. Live your own life the way *you* want to live it.'

She said hesitantly, 'In a week, all being well, we'll be going back to the mainland.'

'A lot can happen in a week.' His tone had lightened again, almost deliberately. 'A day at a time, that's the way we take it.'

If her mind had been ready to reject that offer her body certainly wasn't, Vanessa acknowledged fatalistically as he let her go. A day at a time—it was as good a philosophy as any. At the very least she would have the experience to look back on.

Regardless, it cost her an effort to face her father again after lunch. He was looking a little stronger, although still finding it a strain to talk for too long.

'You won't go back to Caledonia without me, will you?' he asked fretfully at one point. 'I don't want to be left here on my own.'

'I don't have any intention of leaving,' Vanessa assured him. 'But neither should you let this thing with Raoul disturb you. I told you what he said. He stopped bearing grudges.'

His head moved on the pillow. 'You don't know him.'

'Are you sure you do?' she questioned gently. 'Why don't you see him, let him tell you himself?'

The gaunt features tautened. 'I don't want to see him. It's enough to be forced into accepting his hospitality at all. The minute I can get out of this bed you're to get Brenden back here with the boat.'

'Doctor Renaud said at least a week before you could

even contemplate the journey.' Vanessa tried to keep her tone steady and calming. 'It might be dangerous to go against advice.'

'I'm the best judge of how I feel.' His eyes searched hers, taking on some new expression in the process. 'Vanessa, don't let him get to you. You wouldn't be the first by a long chalk!'

It was obvious who he was talking about. To pretend otherwise would simply be laying herself open to suspicion. Guilt warmed her cheeks. She had to hope it didn't show.

'I'm not that impressionable,' she said, and wondered why her tongue didn't cleave to the roof of her mouth. 'Just concentrate on getting well, Dad.'

He smiled then for the first time. 'You haven't called me that before.'

She hadn't done so consciously this time, but at least she had succeeded in sidetracking his train of thought. She smiled back, touching his hand. 'Better get used to it.'

'For a little while anyway.' He shook his head again as she started to speak. 'You can't waste your life looking after me. I'm not worth the sacrifice. You have to go home.'

'To marry a man I don't love?'

'There are other men.'

Her throat closed up. Too right there were! It was said that what you never had you never missed, but it wasn't true. This morning she had discovered a hidden part of herself—or more correctly, a part of herself she had been hiding from. She had concluded there was something lacking in her own make-up when Michael had been unable to stir her to any great degree. Now she knew better. All she had needed was the right man. Guilt or no guilt, she couldn't turn away. Not while the choice remained hers to make.

She spent the balance of the afternoon in her room composing a letter to Michael. It was doubly difficult because she didn't want to lie to him, yet neither did she feel able to be totally honest. Telling him about Raoul would serve no purpose. He would simply think of her as a weak-willed fool. He would be right at that, she reflected wryly. She hadn't put up much of a struggle. Yet Raoul had made his point too. She was an adult. She had to be prepared both to make her own decisions and to accept the consequences, no matter what they might be.

Eventually she settled for stating her father's need of her, ignoring the possibility that it might not turn out that way. Michael was going to be hurt anyway, but he would get over it—the same way she would get over Raoul when the time came. That it would come there was little doubt. Not when she really got down to thinking about it. With or without her father, she was no more of Raoul's world than he was of hers. If a week was all she was going to have of him then she would make the most of it. Regret could come later.

Brenden telephoned from Noumea at six. Vanessa took the call in her room. The return journey had been without incident, he reported after first assuring himself that his employer was still on the mend. He was all set to take out their client in the morning. He would have to drop off her things on the way but there would be no time to bring them up to the house, so could she arrange for someone to be waiting to receive them around seven-thirty.

'How are things with you?' he added, sounding faint and faraway. 'Did Raoul leave for the mine yet?'

Until that moment Vanessa had forgotten about the proposed trip. The reminder brought sudden depression. 'Not yet,' she acknowledged. 'How did you know he was supposed to be going?'

'He makes a regular monthly tour of inspection. Everybody knows that. I'd have thought it would make things more comfortable all round if he got himself out of the way for a day or two.'

'It's his island,' she responded. 'I suppose he'll go when he's ready. He leaves Dad alone anyway. Dad wants it that way.'

'Still feeling the strain, is he? Can't say I blame him. A situation like this one would tax a healthy man much less a sick one!'

Brenden knew more about that situation than he had initially made out, Vanessa thought drily after he had rung off. What he believed was something else again. It mattered little now anyway. In becoming involved with Raoul herself she had made it impossible ever to offer him that financial compensation she had contemplated. In all probability he would have refused to accept it regardless. Money had only been a minor part of the issue.

With little of her own still to choose from, and none of it suitable to the evening, she was forced to take stock of the garments which had been hung ready in the fitted wardrobe, finally settling for a black and white figured silk which fell in tiny pleats from the shoulder line. The sandals that went with the dress proved a better fit than the mules she had worn yesterday. Looking at her reflection in the long mirror, she had to concede that fine feathers made all the difference. The dress was beautifully cut, the style so classically simple yet so right for the occasion. Washed under the shower and brushed dry, her hair curled softly about her head, shining copper in the lamplight. If only her face weren't quite so ordinary, she thought, studying the wide brow, the small straight nose, the curve of her mouth. Odd how a fraction of an inch here and there could mean so much. What did Raoul see in her compared with the kind of woman he was no doubt accustomed to having around him? What was the quality that had drawn him, if he was to be believed, the very first time he had laid eyes on her?

She had to cut out this self-criticism, she told herself firmly at that point. It might be the opposite of vanity, but it was no more commendable. If Raoul found her desirable—and it was obvious that he did—then why question the fact? Enjoy it while it lasted.

Raoul was outside on the terrace when she went down at eight-thirty. He invited her to a seat in one of the comfortably padded, semi-reclining chairs while he mixed the martini she asked for at the bar built into the rear wall of the house. He brought two glasses with him when he returned, handing her one and leaning his weight against one of the stone pillars supporting the honeysuckle-covered roof struts.

'I thought we'd eat outside tonight,' he said, indicating the table already prepared. His smile was lazy, knotting her stomach muscles. 'Dinner *à deux*. What better way to spend an evening?'

A preliminary to the night to come. He didn't need to say it; it was right there in his eyes. He was wearing a pale cream jacket and dark slacks, the collar of his shirt open at the throat on that same glint of gold. Vanessa had a fleeting vision of him standing over her in the hut on the beach so few hours ago, and felt the breath catch in her throat. She wished suddenly and desperately that he would pull her up right now into his arms. She needed to be close to him, to feel his body responding to her the way it had done earlier. Reassurance it was called. Not that Raoul would feel the same need. He already knew his own power.

'You've been with your father this afternoon?' he asked.

Vanessa nodded. 'We had tea together. He's eating quite well.'

'It wasn't his stomach that suffered the attack. Another day or so and he may be able to think about getting up for short periods.'

'He's talking about getting out of bed tomorrow,' she said.

'Is he?' There was a pause, then Raoul shrugged. 'He has to know his own strength.'

'I don't think it's that so much as feeling he has to remove himself from Ile Royale as soon as humanly possible. I've tried to convince him he's being foolish but he won't listen.' She hesitated before tagging on, 'I know it's a lot to ask considering, but perhaps if you talked to him . . .'

The lean features showed little reaction. 'I think that would be the last thing he'd want. Pierre Renaud is the one to talk sense into him, if anyone at all.'

'I suppose so.' There was nothing else to say. The refusal had been couched in reasonable terms but it was still a refusal. She took in a breath of the still, scented air, deliberately lightening her tone. 'It's difficult to believe we were in the middle of a storm only twenty-four hours ago. Do they happen often?'

'Not very.' He tilted his glass, looking at the contents with a certain irony about his mouth. 'What is it you say about an ill-wind?'

'It blows nobody any good.' She didn't look at him. 'You think it was—an ill-wind, I mean?'

'It depends on what we make of the opportunity provided. Do you have any regrets over what happened this morning?'

If she did, Vanessa thought wryly, it wasn't in the

way he meant. 'No,' she said.

'That makes two of us. So perhaps the wind was not so ill after all.' He finished off his drink and straightened. 'I think we should eat.'

The meal was served by the inscrutable Lan. 'A national characteristic,' Raoul observed over coffee when the girl had left them alone again. 'I'm never sure what any of them are thinking.'

'It doesn't bother you?' Vanessa asked.

'No, why should it? They lead their lives, I lead mine. Lan will be moving to the mainland when she marries next month. Her husband-to-be owns a small business. Thi-Sen will already have a replacement picked out.'

'Thi-Sen?'

'The matriarch of the family. She's the one who keeps an eye on your father. By her own choice incidentally. She regards it as her duty to minister to those in need.'

'I'm grateful to her. How old would you say she was?'

'Perhaps around sixty. A venerable age by Vietnamese standards. Very few would have lived that long in their own country, even before the communists came into power.'

She said in quick sympathy, 'It must be a terrible feeling to know they can never go back.'

'Better than never having left.' The blue eyes studied her a moment. 'Could you abandon your country the way your father did?'

'It was hardly abandonment,' she protested. 'He's still a British subject.'

'I think you'll find he exchanged that status for French citizenship several years ago.'

It took Vanessa several seconds to rally from that piece of news. 'I suppose it made sense,' she said at length, attempting to be rational about it. 'If he'd made his home here.' She looked up swiftly as the thought occurred. 'You're saying I'd be expected to do the same if I stay?'

Raoul lifted his shoulders. 'It would depend on how permanent an arrangement you intended it to be. What about your mother? Doesn't she merit consideration?'

'She died last year. I thought you knew that already.'

'How could I unless you told me?' he asked reasonably enough. His gaze still rested on her face, slightly narrowed as if in contemplation. 'There's no one else?'

'No.' The denial was premature perhaps considering she hadn't yet despatched the letter to Michael, but she had no intention of bringing his name into it. 'I sold the house a few weeks ago and moved into a flat. The money is invested where I can get at it fairly easily when needed. I was hoping there might be enough to buy or lease some kind of property in Noumea.'

'And then?'

It was Vanessa's turn to shrug. 'A job if possible.'

'You have it all planned out.' There was a pause before he asked, 'Is your father in agreement?'

She hesitated briefly, reluctant to tell another outright lie. 'He's afraid of becoming a burden, but it won't be like that. I'm not making any sacrifces to stay with him.'

'He may not want you to stay. Have you thought about that?'

'Then he'll have to make it clear.'

He made no answer. She supposed there was no answer to make. Looking into the vivid eyes, she felt the tension between them subtly change form; felt her limbs turn suddenly weak.

'You said you were due to visit the mine in the next couple of days,' she said, making an effort to sound casual about it. 'How long will it take?'

'I usually stay over at the manager's house,' Raoul acknowledged. 'But there's no vital reason why the trip shouldn't be postponed for a few days more.' His smile acknowledged the flicker of expression across her face. 'There's no vital reason why I should visit the mine at all, except that I prefer to be *au fait* with all aspects of Company business. Keeping a finger on the pulse, as they say.' He reached out and took her hand, turning it over in his palm to lift it to his lips and press a light kiss to the inside of her wrist. 'I think we are both of us ready for bed, yes?'

'Together?' The question came low.

'Of course together. Did you imagine I might have changed my mind?'

She stiffened just a fraction, voice hardening. 'Did it occur to you I might have changed mine?'

He released the hand he held and straightened, mouth suddenly sardonic. 'My apologies. It's a woman's right to do that, naturally.'

Vanessa gazed at him, already regretting the too hasty retort. 'I didn't say I had.'

'You simply wanted the option?' Raoul shook his head, lip still curled. 'I don't play those games any longer. Either we're of the same mind or we forget this morning ever happened.'

The hurt went too deep to ignore. She said bitterly, 'I suppose you'd find that easy enough!'

'No,' he said, 'I shouldn't find it easy. I was using the term in a purely figurative sense.' He paused, regard speculative. 'What is it you want me to say?'

'Nothing.' The denial was instinctive. 'I was being juvenile.'

For a moment he continued to look at her, as if waiting for more. When he did speak it was quite levelly. 'Perhaps you'd like to look in on your father before retiring for the night.'

'I think so.' She adopted the same tone. 'I spoiled everything, didn't I?'

'Not everything,' he said. 'Just the moment. Perhaps I did take a little too much for granted.' He pushed back his chair and got to his feet, coming round the table to render her an impersonal assistance. 'Go and pay your visit. The rest can wait.'

Until when? Vanessa wondered, but couldn't bring herself to ask. Raoul's mood was uncertain, his whole demeanour altered. If he had lost interest in her as a worthwhile pursuit she had only herself to blame for blowing hot and cold the way she had.

Her father was asleep, his breathing irregular. She stayed to watch him for some minutes but there was no change. Doctor Renaud would be here the day after tomorrow. Perhaps it would be better all round if her father managed to persuade him that he was fit enough to withstand the journey back to the mainland. It would at least save her from making any further errors of judgment.

It was barely eleven when she reached her own room. She took her time preparing for bed, sliding between crisp cool sheets at last to switch off the lamp and lie with resolutely closed eyes willing sleep to claim her. Had she simply allowed things to happen as they would, Raoul would be right here with her. She could console herself with the thought that it was better like this, but she couldn't make herself believe it down deep where it mattered. Her whole body ached for him.

The minutes ticked by inexorably. Midnight came and went. Eventually she dozed, waking again with a start some unknown time later when the door softly opened. Raoul came over to the bed as she pressed herself upright, pausing at the end of it. He was wearing a lightweight robe, his chest bare beneath it. The shaft of moonlight revealed his lower face yet left his eyes in shadow.

'I want you,' he stated without equivocation. 'I can't sleep for wanting you!' He was sliding out of the robe as he spoke, letting it fall to the floor at his feet. 'I won't let you say no to me, Vanessa.'

She had no intention. Not with her every sense alight, her heartbeats like thunder in her ears. She went into his arms like a homing pigeon when he slid into the bed at her side, feeling his warmth and hardness envelop her.

CHAPTER FIVE

NEAL Grantham was up and dressed when Doctor Renaud arrived on the Thursday, refusing to admit to any weakness yet all too obviously suffering from it. Only with great difficulty was he finally persuaded to wait out the weekend before undertaking the trip to the mainland.

'He must take only limited exercise over the next few days,' the Frenchman advised Vanessa when they were alone. 'It is going to be up to you to make him see the sense in coming to the clinic for further tests.'

'Do you have some doubt about his chances of a full recovery?' she asked, trying to be practical about it.

His hesitation was fleeting. 'In all coronary cases there's an element of doubt. I'll feel happier when I have a more detailed picture of the damage done.'

'He'll be there,' she promised. 'Even if I have to drag him!'

He smiled a little. 'Your father is a lucky man to have someone who cares so much. If all goes well he should be fit enough to travel on Monday. I'll expect to see him on Tuesday. In the meantime, remember, he should take care not to overdo anything.'

Saying it was one thing, Vanessa reflected, putting the advice into practice quite another. They were dealing with a man who was still virtually a stranger to her. In some ways, Brenden was closer to him than she was.

The latter had telephoned each evening, eager to assure her that he was coping quite adequately on his own. Getting rid of a source of income might not be such a good idea, Vanessa was bound to acknowledge. At least while Brenden was still around to bear the brunt. It wasn't going to be up to her to make the ultimate decision, in any case. That much she had to concede. No matter how he had obtained her, the *Julia* was in her father's name.

He was sitting by the opened window when she returned to his room. He looked round at her with a faint smile.

'Just getting a few lungfuls of fresh air. It feels good. Did the medic leave yet?'

'He went to see Raoul first,' she said. 'How are you feeling?'

'I'll be better when I get out of this place.' He held up a hand as she started to speak. 'All right, I'm not going back on what we agreed. It's for my own good, I'll accept that. Only until Monday though.'

Even that small speech had left him short of breath, Vanessa could see. She said placatingly, 'Only until Monday. I'll tell Brenden to come and fetch us—providing he doesn't have a charter. He seems to be managing quite well on his own.'

'If that's the same kind of hint Renaud was dropping, the answer is definitely no,' Neal responded. 'I'll keep off the bottle but I'm not letting anyone else take over the boat. She's all I've got.'

'You have me,' she said levelly. 'If you really want me to go I'll go, but you'll have to tell me.'

The grizzled head moved slowly from side to side. 'What kind of a life would it be for you here? What about the friends you must have back home—this man you were telling me about?'

'Family is more important.' Impulsively she dropped to her knees at the side of his chair, taking his hand to lay her cheek against it for a moment. 'Dad, I want to stay. I really do! I can make a home for us both. You don't have to give up the *Julia*. All I'm asking is that you move ashore to live. Would that be so difficult for you?'

'I don't know,' he admitted. 'It's been a long time since I had anyone else to consider.' He looked down at her, eyes softening. 'You're so much like your mother. Even your hair is the same colour, although she always wore hers long.' His lips twisted suddenly. 'At least she did when I was with her. I did a shameful thing leaving her that way—leaving you both that way.'

'She'd be glad to know we were together now.' Vanessa could feel she was winning. 'Don't think about it anymore. Let's start from here.'

The same words Raoul had used to her, she realised, yet she was no more certain now of how far he meant their relationship to go than she had been then. She had lived these past forty-eight hours in a kind of dreamworld, taking not just each day but each and every moment as it came. As a lover, Raoul could have few equals. In his arms she was another person. Whatever happened after she left the island, life would never be the same.

Pierre Renaud stayed to eat lunch. Although his command of English was good, the doctor was obviously more at ease in his own language, responding with alacrity to Vanessa's suggestion that a little practice wouldn't do her any harm.

'You have the ear,' he commented at one stage. 'It won't be long before we have you speaking the language like a native. Raoul should make it a rule to speak only in French while you stay here. It's the best way of learning.'

'I'll think about it,' promised the latter on a lazy note. 'Practice, as they say, makes for perfection.' Blue eyes found green, a taunt in their depths. 'You wouldn't find it too much of a strain?'

Vanessa shook her head, hoping the other man wasn't too good at recognising innuendo when he heard it. 'I'd enjoy the challenge.'

Saying goodbye to the doctor later, she wondered just how much he had guessed of the situation. There had been moments when she had caught him watching her with an odd expression, as if weighing her in balance. No doubt if he did suspect the truth of the matter he would consider that Raoul was simply amusing himself with this unsophisticated English girl. He could easily be right too, she thought wryly, although it made little difference to the way she felt. She could no more say no to Raoul now than fly.

They spent the afternoon down at the cove in the dim privacy of the little changing hut. Lying there with her cheek resting on Raoul's bare chest in the lazy aftermath, Vanessa allowed her mind to drift, imagining how it might be if they were together on a lasting basis. Did desire fade with time and familiarity? she wondered. Could any two people hope to retain such vibrant intensity? The only married couple she could number among her closer friends had become so casual in their attitude towards each other lately, although it was barely two years since their wedding.

'You're thinking deep thoughts again,' Raoul observed, shifting his position a little. 'Dare I ask what they might be?'

'I was thinking how nice it would be to have a swim,' she improvised swiftly. 'Only we didn't bring any bathing things with us.'

His laugh mocked her. 'Why would we need them?'

'Because someone might see us.'

'No one else comes here.' He sat up, lifting her with him. 'It sounds a refreshing idea. It's been a long time since I swam in the nude.'

'We call it skinny-dipping,' she said with assumed nonchalance. 'I did it once myself when I was about sixteen.'

Dark brows flicked upwards. 'So young and yet so daring! Was the company mixed?'

'Yes, but there was nothing sexual about it. At least, not on the surface.' She smiled at the memory. 'To tell the truth, I think we were all of us too self-conscious to look at one another. It was just sheer bravado, that's all.'

'You still have the same inhibitions?'

'A little,' she confessed.

The blue eyes dropped pointedly to her breasts, his smile provocative. 'I would never have guessed.'

'This is different,' she protested, stilling the sudden ridiculous urge to cover herself from his gaze.

'Because of the lack of light perhaps?'

'Not wholly. It's . . .' She stopped there, making a small helpless gesture. 'You wouldn't understand.'

'Few men could,' came the dry response. He waited a moment more, then smiled and got to his feet, holding out a hand to her. 'We'll go together.'

It was only few yards across the beach to the water's edge. Reaching it, Vanessa was seized by some sudden impulse, running ahead of him to splash through the shallows and dive beneath the surface. Raoul caught up with her before she was halfway out to the net, dragging her to him to enclose her between hard-hewn thighs as they went under, his mouth sealing her breath. She was gasping when they surfaced again, her ears popping.

'You're mad!' she exclaimed, treading water to keep herself upright. 'You could have drowned us both!'

'You provoked me,' he said, eyes glinting as he matched her movements. 'I'm no sixteen year old youth!'

And she no innocent either, Vanessa was bound to concede. Not anymore. Michael wouldn't know her this way. She wasn't even sure he would want to know her this way. Raoul had opened her mind; made her aware. Whether he had done her any favour was another matter entirely. Certainly she would never be content to settle for anything less than what she had known with him.

They made love again when they returned to the hut, the moisture drying on them in the sun-baked heat. Raoul was the first to stir, his breath warm on her cheek as he raised himself to look down at her.

'I have to leave in the morning,' he said with regret.

It took a moment for Vanessa to find her voice. She did her best to sound matter-of-fact about it. 'For how long?'

'Three days, perhaps longer. It depends on what I find.'

'You're going to the mine?'

'No,' he said. 'To Kalgoorlie. I received the call this morning while you were with your father.'

She said slowly, 'I didn't realise you had any contact with . . . her.'

'Her name is Elise,' he supplied. 'My father left them well enough provided for financially, but the trust is administered by the estate. As executor I'm responsible for their welfare.' He added unemotionally, 'It seems she was taken ill—may even die. I have to make arrangements for her sons in the event of that happening.'

'You mean to bring them here?'

Something flared in his eyes. He thrust himself abruptly away from her to sit up, arms resting on his bent knees. 'That will never happen. Not while I'm alive to stop it!'

'I'm sorry.' She scarcely knew what else to say. 'I wasn't trying to suggest you should.'

There was a pause, then he shrugged. 'I have difficulty retaining a sense of proportion on the subject. Those boys don't even bear the DuTemple name yet they could one day inherit everything.'

Unless he himself married and produced a child, came the fleeting thought. 'We'll have left before you get back,' she said, keeping a tight rein on her inflection.

'Yes, I know.' He sounded rueful. 'It isn't the way I would have wanted it. I don't have the choice. You have to see that.'

'Of course.' She came upright, making an effort to pull herself together. It wasn't as if she hadn't known there had to be an end sometime. 'I understand, Raoul.'

'Naturally I'll be in contact when I do get back,' he added after a moment when he appeared to be waiting for her to say something else. 'You'll be staying at the same place initially, I take it?'

'I imagine so.' She didn't believe a word, but there was no point in underlining the fact. The situation was awkward enough as it was. Pride drew a smile on her lips. 'I hope everything works out for you.'

He made no move to stop her when she reached out for her things, waiting until she was almost dressed before saying softly, 'We still have tonight.'

'Yes, we do, don't we?' Vanessa kept her voice deliberately light. To turn away from him now would be too much of a give-away. She had to play out her role to the bitter end. 'We'd better make the most of it.'

She spent the rest of the day trying to do just that; finding some kind of refuge in the pretence that none of this went any deeper with her than it obviously did with Raoul. Her father received the news of his host's impending departure with unconcealed relief.

'It's better that we don't have to meet,' he said. 'It would have been awkward for both of us. I might even make it downstairs over the weekend. I need to start finding my legs again. It's surprising how weakening a few days in bed can be.'

'Don't overdo it,' Vanessa begged. 'It hasn't been a week yet.'

'I won't,' he promised. 'Stop worrying about me. I'm going to be fine.'

'You will go to see Doctor Renaud though, won't you?' she insisted, and heard him sigh.

'If it will set your mind at rest, though I doubt there's a need. Other people my age have come through worse.' He gave her a shrewd glance. 'You're looking peaked yourself, if it comes to that. Not coming down with anything, are you?'

She forced a smile. 'Too much sun. I'm not used to it. Did you want another book bringing up?'

If he recognised the change of subject as deliberate he allowed himself no comment. Even if she had been prepared to tell him the truth, Vanessa doubted if he would really want to know. She had got into this affair on her own, and it was up to her to get over it. Time was all she needed.

She awoke at daybreak when Raoul slid from her bed, lying motionless as he pulled on the short silk robe.

'I ordered the launch for seven,' he said softly, sensing her regard. He came back to the bed, seating himself on the edge of the mattress in order to reach her mouth with his, the kiss lingering, tinged with genuine regret. 'I hate leaving you this way,' he acknowledged, 'but circumstances force me. You'll let me know where you are?'

'Why don't we just say goodbye and leave it at that?' Vanessa asked huskily, and saw his expression undergo a sudden unreadable change.

'Is that what you'd prefer?'

'It isn't so much a case of what I'd prefer but of what's going to be practical,' she got out. 'You have your life to lead, and I have mine. There's no way they're going to overlap.'

It was a moment or two before he replied. When he did speak it was on an oddly restrained note. 'It wouldn't be easy, I have to agree.'

'It would be impossible.' She was fighting to stay on top of her emotions. 'It's been a wonderful three days, Raoul. Don't let's spoil them.'

His mouth twisted a little. 'No, that would be a pity.' He paused, regard narrowed to her face as if attempting to plumb the depths of her mind, then he pushed himself abruptly to his feet. 'You're right, of course,' he said. 'We were neither of us under any illusions when we began this. So, we'll be practical about it, as you say. No prolonged goodbyes.'

So what had she expected? Vanessa asked herself dully, resisting the desperate desire to call him back as he moved away towards the door. She had known all along that the end had to come. If she hadn't made it easy for him she would only have been storing up heartache for herself. This way she would at least entertain no false hopes.

Regardless, a last faint spark still lingered, extinguished only after the door had finally closed. There had been no second thoughts on Raoul's part; not even a last glance. By the time he returned from Kalgoorlie she would not only be out of his life but also out of his mind. She had to teach herself to forget him too, but it wasn't going to be as quick a process. The pain inside her was too intense.

The weekend dragged. Vanessa spent much of it walking, exploring the more immediate regions of the island as far as the cluster of neat white houses which formed a regular village on the lower slopes of the ridge. The Vietnamese were not antagonistic, simply aloof. They had their own boat in which they travelled backwards and forwards to the mainland as and when they wished. In many ways it seemed an idyllic life. Certainly they were unoppressed. Most of the time they had the island entirely to themselves.

Neal took his first trip downstairs on the Sunday morning, delighted to be out and about.

'I'll feel even better come Monday,' he stated over a light lunch on the terrace. 'Although it's easier knowing our host isn't here.' His gaze came to rest on his daughter's face, his smile fading a little. 'You've been so listless this last couple of days. Are you sure you're feeling well?'

Vanessa summoned a smile of her own, taking herself to task for not putting on a better act. 'Boredom,' she said lightly. 'I'm as ready as you are to leave the place. Brenden will be here by ten o'clock. He already arranged a short-term lease on an apartment not too far from the quayside.'

'I already know all that.' There was a pause and a change of tone. 'It isn't my place to ask, considering you're not a little girl anymore, but did anything happen between you and Raoul?'

Her heart jerked. 'Such as what?'

'Such as his taking advantage of the fact that you're my daughter, for instance. A handy weapon to use against a man when all else fails.'

The same thought had occurred to her on the beach that first morning, yet not since. She refuted the possibility now. 'There was nothing like that. You're obsessed with this retaliation threat he made.'

He said wryly, 'You could be right. I still can't believe he'd just forget the whole thing.'

'If he hadn't before he certainly has now.'

'I'll take your word for it.'

He remained unconvinced about anything she had said, and they both knew it. Vanessa could only be grateful that he didn't try to pursue the subject. Anything that had taken place between her and Raoul had been as much at her instigation as his. She had put up no more than a token struggle. Where she had failed was in allowing her emotions to become involved, and that was something only time would alter.

She went for a final swim in the cove while Neal rested that afternoon, giving the knife a masochistic twist. The little hut was dim and cool and full of images. She stayed there for a while, her whole body one vast ache as she recalled every intimate detail. They had been so attuned, so totally complete together. Looking back, it was difficult to believe that Raoul himself had felt nothing beyond simple physical lust. Yet if he had, what good did it do her? If he married at all it would be to a woman from his own world. The wonder was that he had put it off for so long when a son was so essential to the continuation of his line.

Her father was still fast asleep on the lounger when she got back to the house. She went through to go upstairs and change, freezing with one foot already resting on the first tread as a stunning, blonde-haired young woman appeared in the library doorway.

'Lan told me you were around somewhere,' stated the newcomer. 'I didn't want to disturb your father. It seems Raoul had to leave quite suddenly?'

'That's right.' Vanessa was totally at a loss. 'Are you . . . a friend of his?'

The smile held a sudden hint of mockery. 'I'm his stepsister, only don't let that throw you. The relationship is purely academic.' Crystal's tone altered. 'You're here until tomorrow, right?'

'Right,' Vanessa said again. 'I gather you already heard why we're here in the first place?'

'The bare bones of the story, that's all. A heart attack, wasn't it?' She didn't bother to wait for confirmation. 'That must have put Raoul in something of a dilemma.

Vanessa said carefully, 'You know my father?'

'Know of. We never met.' Eyes the colour of topaz registered disparagement. 'There was never any mention of a family.'

'I only arrived in New Caledonia a couple of weeks ago.' Vanessa saw no reason to expound on that statement. It was already apparent that the other was aware of the main factors. 'I'm sorry to land you with such an awkward situation, but there isn't a great deal I can do about it before the boat comes for us tomorrow.'

'No, well, I daresay I can live with it till then. Shall you be coming down to dinner tonight?'

'I usually do.' Vanessa looked back at her steadily. 'If you'd rather I had a tray upstairs . . .'

One elegant, scarlet-tipped hand came up in a gesture of negation. 'Heaven forbid that I should be less hospitable than Raoul! I was just making sure so I could tell them in the kitchen.'

And to underline her own position here as mistress of the house in Raoul's absence, thought Vanessa wryly. Not that there had been any doubt about that to start with. Her arrival had not been scheduled or Raoul would surely have mentioned it. She could appreciate what a shock it must have been for her to find her stepbrother gone and the Granthams in possession.

'I'll go and dress,' she said. 'Then I'll see about getting my father back up to his room. Today was his first time downstairs since it happened.'

'He made a remarkable recovery.' Crystal was already turning back into the library. 'We'll meet again later then.'

Vanessa continued on her way, limbs heavy. Less than twenty-four hours more and they would have been away. She didn't want to spend any time with Raoul's stepsister, yet it was inevitable that she should. The reason for her reluctance was not difficult to discover. A simple way of putting it could be 'fear of what she might find out'. Crystal herself had implanted the question mark with that over-emphatic denial of any blood relationship between her and Raoul. Why would she have bothered had their regard for each other been that of brother and sister? The other girl was everything she, Vanessa, would like to be; beautiful, poised, able to take things in her stride. Had she been asked to list the qualities that might draw a man like Raoul to a woman then Crystal would have them all.

She was being ridiculous, the rational part of her mind pointed out at that juncture. Right or wrong, the matter had little bearing on her own situation. She wouldn't be seeing Raoul again anyway.

There was no sign of the newcomer when she went downstairs again, although the library doors stood open. Neal was awake but alone. He received the news without comment other than to reiterate his thankfulness to be returning to more familiar surroundings the next day.

'I think I'm ready to go back up,' he added. 'Are you going to have tea with me as usual?'

'Of course.' Vanessa stopped herself from moving forward to offer him a hand as he got to his feet, recognising his need for independance. 'I'll go and tell Lan where we'll be.'

The latter was through in the big, sparklingly modern kitchen with Thi-Sen. They were talking together quietly. Judging from the way they broke off the conversation when she appeared in the doorway, Vanessa suspected the subject of it might well have been herself. On the other hand, she conceded, as the older woman serenely returned her greeting, it could well be that she was becoming over-sensitive all the way down the line!

Lan's response to her request was, as always, brief and unsmiling. She for one would shed no tears when the houseguests left. Vanessa wished they could go now, but it was impossible of course. Even if her father was both ready and willing it was far too late to consider fetching Brenden out to Roayale today.

The afternoon turned into evening, the sunset a crimson glory. Dressed in her favourite blue cotton, Vanessa went down around eight-thirty to find Crystal already seated out on the terrace with a drink to hand. She was wearing a simple sheath of a dress in a cream slub silk, her hair scooped into a smooth chignon. Vanessa wondered if the colour was natural.

'I don't want anything thanks,' she said when the

invitation was extended. She took a seat herself, searching her mind for something to say and finding nothing but a blank.

Crystal took the onus from her. 'If I'd known Raoul wasn't going to be here I wouldn't have bothered coming over. There was nothing said about his leaving Royale when I rang through yesterday.'

'You spoke to him?' Vanessa asked.

'Well hardly, or he'd have warned me himself. I thought he'd be on the mainland. When they told me he was here I decided to surprise him.' She paused, frowning a little. 'Did he say where he was going?'

'Kalgoorlie,' Vanessa supplied, and heard the sudden indrawn breath.

'He swore he'd never ...' She broke off abruptly, waiting a moment or two before adding on a more controlled note, 'I guess you heard the whole tale. From Raoul, or from your father?'

'From both.' Vanessa hesitated. 'There are two sides to every story.'

'Try telling that to Raoul.'

'I already did.'

'Oh?' Crystal sounded nonplussed. 'So what was your father's version?'

Green eyes met amber, holding steady. 'Raoul agreed we should put it all behind us. I think he was right.'

The full red mouth hardened a fraction. 'Are you sure this whole thing wasn't staged to that end?'

'If you're doubting whether my father really did suffer a heart attack you only need ask Doctor Renaud,' Vanessa responded, trying to stay cool and calm about it. 'Or would you suspect him of being in on it too?'

'Pierre Renaud?' Crystal's laugh was lacking in humour. 'Hardly likely, I admit. It's still an incredible coincidence that you just happened to finish up on Royale.'

'We needed oxygen, and Royale was closer than the mainland at the time.'

'Yes, well, I'll take your word for it.' The pause was studied. 'So let's talk about Raoul instead. Tell me, do you make a habit of going to bed with men you barely know?' She smiled contemptuously as the involuntary wave of colour swept Vanessa's face. 'So I was right about that, at least. I can usually tell the women he's had. They always sound so proprietary about him.'

'The way you do?' Vanessa countered, and saw her opponent's expression tauten.

'Except that I have good reason. You see, he's going to marry me.'

The apartment Brenden had rented turned out to be the ground floor of an old converted house on one of Noumea's back streets. With two bedrooms, bathroom, kitchen and large salon, space was not limited. Vanessa was delighted to discover they also had use of the walled garden.

'It's only for a couple of months,' Brenden warned. 'The whole place is going on the market. At least it's going to give you time to look around.'

Buying something like this wouldn't be a bad idea, Vanessa reflected, stepping out through folding doors in need of a coat of new paint on to the stone-paved patio. They could lease the top floor to defray expenses. It was worth thinking about. The scent from the honeysuckle spilling over the nearby wall caught at her throat, bringing back memories she would have preferred to leave hidden. Tomorrow or the next day Raoul would return to find his fiancée waiting for him. Unofficial the engagement might be, but she had no reason to doubt Crystal's word. If she could make herself hate him it would help, only the fault had been as much hers as his. Had she rejected him that very first morning on the beach he would have left her alone.

'Neal's lying down,' said Brenden quietly, coming up behind her. 'Van, I'm worried about him. He got over it so much faster last time.'

She went very still as the words penetrated, eyes searching his with growing alarm. 'You mean this isn't the first attack he's had?'

'He didn't tell you?' Regret clouded his features. 'Damn, I should have known!'

'How long ago?' she demanded.

'A few months. It wasn't all that long after he took me on.'

'Is that the reason you stayed?'

Brenden shifted uncomfortably. 'Part of it, I suppose. Only it's different now. I don't feel the need to move on anymore, so don't imagine I'll be making any sacrifices. I can cope with the *Julia* as long as necessary.'

'Thanks.' Her voice was husky. 'You're a good friend to have.' Vanessa glanced back indoors, brows drawn together. 'Doctor Renaud asked me to get him to the clinic tomorrow. Who was his doctor before?'

'He didn't have one.' Brenden made a gesture of apology. 'He wouldn't let me send for anyone. It wasn't as bad as this time. Like I said, he seemed to get over it quite quickly.'

'But he still carried on drinking too much.'

'Only at weekends, which was an improvement on every other night.' There was another helpless gesture. 'What could I do except hang around and keep an eye on him? This time was different. He didn't have any choice.'

And next time? Vanessa felt her throat close up. If there was a next time it would probably be the last. Now, more than ever, they needed medical advice.

Regardless, it took all her persuasive powers to get her father to keep the appointment. In the end he agreed because it was, as he wearily said, the only way he was going to get some peace. Modern and luxurious, the clinic occupied a large plot of ground on the outskirts of the town. Approaching it by taxi, Vanessa knew a certain concern over what all this was going to cost, although money had to be of secondary importance to her father's health. The time to think about it was later when the bills started coming in. By then she hoped to have effected the transfer of funds from England.

The whole place was designed like an up-market hotel, the decor and furnishings lacking any hint of hospital austerity. Pierre Renaud met them in the imposing lobby.

'I'm glad you came,' he said, eyes scanning his patient's face. 'I had some doubt that you would.'

'I'm only here because my daughter insisted,' Neal admitted. 'I feel fine.'

The Frenchman's glance flickered briefly to Vanessa and back again, expression revealing little. 'Even so, it was wiser. If you would like to come with me.' To Vanessa he added, 'Please make yourself comfortable. Coffee will be brought to you shortly.'

It was pleasant sitting there relaxed in the comfortable chair with the air-conditioning humming around her—at least for the first hour. By midday, Vanessa had given up attempting to lose herself in a magazine, watching the corridor up which Doctor Renaud and her father had disappeared with the worry growing steadily inside her. There had been no intimation that it would take this long to do a few simple tests. Something was wrong—had to be wrong. If only someone would come and tell her!

The doctor returned at last, but he was alone. Vanessa was on her feet long before he reached her, moving to meet him.

'I want to keep him here for a few days,' he said without preamble. 'Will you speak to him and try to persuade him?'

'I'll try.' Her mouth had gone dry. 'He told you about the previous attack?'

His gaze sharpened. 'No, he didn't, but it would explain the extent of the damage. Why wasn't I informed last week?'

'I only found out myself last night. Apparently he refused to seek medical attention at the time.'

'As so many before him. They convince themselves it was simply indigestion!' He looked at her a moment, the professional mask dissolving. 'You're too intelligent a person not to recognise the implications. After two attacks there's a much increased probability of another. However, providing your father places himself in our hands now there's a chance we can prolong his expectations.'

Her voice came out thickly. 'For how long?'

'A few months, perhaps. There's no certainty.'

'And if he leaves without treatment?' She watched his head move slowly from side to side, biting her lip. 'All right, I'll talk to him.'

They walked the length of the corridor in silence. The doctor took her to the door of the ante-room where his patient was waiting and left her to it, saying he would be back in twenty minutes. Neal was fully dressed and standing at the wide window.

'Good view of the lagoon,' he said without turning.

'We could go down and pay Brenden a call after we leave here. He doesn't have anything booked till tomorrow.'

Vanessa said softly, 'Doctor Renaud wants me to persuade you to stay here for a few days.'

He turned then, expression set in lines of determination. 'I know he does, only it isn't going to happen. It's too late to start grasping at straws.'

'It's never too late,' she protested desperately. 'There's so much they can do these days.'

'Like finding me a new heart?' He smiled a little. 'Even if we could afford that kind of surgery I'd be too old for it to be practical.'

'If only you'd been hospitalised the first time!' she burst out, breaking every ground rule she had laid down for herself. 'Why didn't you let Brenden fetch you a doctor then, Dad?'

'He shouldn't have told you.' The gaunt face had darkened. 'He wasn't supposed to tell anybody!'

'You're not answering the question.'

'No.' He looked at her broodingly. 'Why? I suppose because I didn't think I had anything much worth living for at the time. I'd abandoned everything that was good in my life.' There was a moment's silence, then his expression firmed again. 'Anyway, there isn't much use talking about it now. What's done is done. If the difference is only going to be a matter of months, I'd as soon let nature take its course from here. Once I'm gone you can go on back home and start living your own life again.'

Pain shot through her. 'I suppose,' she said gruffly, 'I should be thankful you're letting me stay at all. You're not planning on moving back on board the *Julia*?'

'Not to sleep.' A smile touched his lips. 'I've got

used to a decent bed again. I might go out with Bren tomorrow though. Just to see how he frames.'

It was his choice, Vanessa told herself dully, and she had to accept it. She conjured a smile of her own. 'I should have known you wouldn't be able to stay away. I'll go and ask them to ring for a taxi.'

Pierre was coming back along the corridor as she left the room. He paused when he saw her, brows lifting in query. 'You made him listen, yes?'

Vanessa shook her head, seeing his expression alter. 'He doesn't consider it's worth the effort.'

The sigh signalled resignation. 'Then that, as you say, is that.' He studied her a moment. 'What will you do?'

'Afterwards?' Vanessa couldn't think that far ahead. 'I'm not sure. Go back to England, I imagine.' She added quickly, 'You must let us know what we owe you, doctor—including those two trips out to Royale.'

'The matter was already dealt with,' he rejoined. 'Raoul . . .'

'We'd prefer to pay our own dues,' she responded tautly. 'He already did enough for us.'

The face in front of her became suddenly impassive. 'Very well. The account will be sent to you.' He extended a hand. 'Say goodbye to your father for me. And remember, if he should change his mind we may still be able to help.'

She could have told him there and then that there would be no change of mind, but why bother? This man was a doctor, dedicated to extending life. He might appreciate her father's viewpoint but it was against his every instinct to come right out and say so. From now on they were on their own.

CHAPTER SIX

THERE were only two mourners at the graveside. It wasn't until it was all over and they were turning away that Vanessa saw the man standing some little distance behind.

'It was kind of you to come, doctor,' she said formally, concealing her surprise.

'I almost failed to get here in time,' Pierre Renaud confessed. 'An appointment impossible to re-arrange. It was only by chance that I saw the newspaper announcement at all.'

'I almost didn't bother putting it in,' she admitted. 'It seemed a waste of time considering his lack of friends.'

'He had you until the end. That must have meant a great deal to him.'

Her smile was wan. 'It wasn't long.'

'I'd better get back to the boat,' Brenden put in. His face looked drawn, the grief still plain in his eyes. 'A half-day charter,' he added for the other man's benefit.

'Life must go on,' agreed the doctor. 'You have transport?'

Brenden glanced at Vanessa. 'You were going to drop me off at the quay.'

'You take the car,' she said. 'I can get the bus. It goes past the gates.'

'When it arrives,' interjected the Frenchman. 'They run to no timetable. 'I must pass your district to return to the clinic. May I offer you a lift?'

99

Vanessa accepted with concealed reluctance, feeling the nausea rising again in her throat. The last thing she wanted was to be ill in front of this man, yet she could hardly refuse the offer. It was barely ten minutes by car to the apartment. Surely she could hang on that long.

Brenden took his leave at the gates. Seated beside her benefactor in the comfortable saloon, Vanessa tried desperately to think of other things—anything to take her mind off the movement. She would probably have felt even worse on board one of the scuttling little blue mini-buses which comprised the transport system in and around Noumea. A mere ten minutes and she would be home.

Home? It was hardly that. One more week and the lease would be up. With her father gone, it was time to start making some decisions. The boat was going to be a big problem. In many ways it would have been better if it had been left to Brenden in entirety instead of just a half share. Persuading him to take over her half too was impossible; he had already made that clear. Yet staying here was even more so. She needed a place where she was totally unknown; where she would be just another statistic. The Australian mainland, perhaps, providing she could obtain the necessary visa. But even then it could only be for a limited period.

It would be simpler all round to return to England. The British Isles weren't so small that she couldn't lose herself. At least there she was assured of a certain security. Which still didn't tell her what to do about the *Julia*.

'You'll be leaving Caledonia soon?' asked the doctor, echoing her thoughts.

'As soon as I can,' she agreed. 'There are a few

things still to be taken care of.' She paused, gulping, aware of the perspiration breaking out on her forehead. It was no use. 'I'm sorry,' she said, 'but could you please stop for a moment. I'm going to be sick.'

He responded at once, pulling into the side of the road. Vanessa got out just in time, afterwards leaning weakly against the door for a moment while her stomach slowly settled, grateful for the lack of passers-by to witness her discomfiture. She had to turn sometime, of course, glancing his way with shamed, apologetic expression as she slid back into her seat. 'I'll be all right now, thanks.'

He made no immediate move to put the vehicle into motion again, his gaze unnervingly shrewd as he scanned her pale face. 'You suffer often from travel sickness?' he asked.

'Not often,' she said. 'I suppose it's reaction. I only had a little time with my father but it doesn't make it any easier.'

'Naturally not.' There was nothing to be gleaned from the smooth response. 'You're sure you feel well enough to continue?'

'Quite sure.' She still felt queasy but they could hardly stay here on this suburban street for the rest of the morning. 'It isn't far now,' she added, as much for her own reassurance as for his.

They made the house without further mishap, though only just. Vanessa was relieved to get out of the car, and somewhat dismayed when Doctor Renaud insisted on seeing her indoors.

'You need a sedative,' he said, holding up the small pill box he had extracted from the leather bag on the rear seat. 'I'll leave you some of these. Do you have a doctor of your own?'

'I don't need a doctor,' she denied swiftly. Too swiftly. 'A regular one, I mean. Would you like some coffee while you're here?'

He smiled then, and nodded. 'That sounds good.'

She could hear him moving about in the living room while she prepared the tray. She hoped he wouldn't be staying for long. His medical training gave him too much of an advantage. The one thing she didn't need was a diagnosis.

He was out on the patio when she went back, the jacket of his dark suit thrown carelessly across a chair. Vanessa had elected not to wear any kind of mourning herself, chiefly because her father had requested that she didn't, yet she appreciated the gesture on his part. It was his reason for attending the funeral at all that she found difficult to understand. He had scarcely known his patient. They had called in one of the local doctors to sign the death certificate, which fact must have occurred to him.

'A substantial building,' he commented when they were both of them seated at the wrought iron table. 'You own it?'

Vanessa shook her head. 'We only leased it. The term is up next weekend.'

'So you'll be staying on at least until then.'

'Probably.'

'And afterwards? Back to England, I think you said?'

'Yes.' She swallowed, wishing he would drink up and go. Her own fault for offering the coffee in the first place, yet she could hardly have done otherwise. 'I still have the return half of my ticket. Dad wouldn't let me trade it in.'

'That was wise of him. The single fare would have cost you a great deal more.' He was watching her face, by no means oblivious to the tension in her. 'You're not drinking your coffee. Do you still feel ill?'

She began to shake her head, and knew she wasn't going to make it. Hurriedly she got to her feet. 'Excuse me,' she muttered, and fled.

He was sitting where she had left him when she finally nerved herself to return. He didn't look at her.

'My wife suffered the same problem with each of her pregnancies during the first few months,' he observed conversationally. 'The condition can be alleviated. You should see a gynaecologist at the earliest opportunity. I can recommend a good man.'

An expensive one too, no doubt, Vanessa thought drily, recalling the bill they had received from the clinic for services rendered. It may be a waste of time denying her condition but she was still capable of handling it.

'I intend to,' she said. 'Only not here. Another week won't hurt anything.'

A frown crossed the thin features. 'How far advanced are you?'

She shrugged, assuming a nonchalance she was far from feeling. 'I've missed two periods, so seven or eight weeks, I imagine.'

'You intend to seek an abortion?'

Her head lifted sharply. 'No!'

His nod neither approved nor disapproved the decision. 'If you intend travelling by air a medical check would be advisable first.'

The heat went out of her, leaving her curiously close to tears. 'All right,' she said wearily. 'I'll see to it.'

'And now you'd like me to go.' It was a statement not a question, the accompanying smile not without sympathy. 'An understandable reaction.' He was on his feet and reaching for his jacket as he spoke. 'If I can be of any help at all you know where to reach me.'

'Yes, I know.' Vanessa had risen with him. 'And thanks again for coming to the cemetery.' She hesitated briefly. 'Why did you?'

He drew on the jacket before answering, taking his time. 'I was asked.'

Her heart skipped a beat. 'By whom?'

'Raoul DuTemple.' The doctor's eyes were on hers, registering her reaction. 'He believed his own presence might not have been welcome. Was he right?'

'Very possibly.' She had recovered her composure, outwardly at least. 'There was no love lost between him and my father. Thank him for the thought when you see him, will you, please? And I hope it didn't disrupt your day too much.'

She stood for several minutes after she closed the door behind the Frenchman, bringing her thoughts to some kind of order. So Raoul hadn't totally forgotten about her; that was something, she supposed. She wondered what his reaction would be if Pierre Renaud passed on the news. If he bothered to check dates, he had to realise who was responsible.

Responsible perhaps, but hardly to be blamed, came the rueful acknowledgement. The fault lay at her own door. Few men in this day and age were going to consider the possibility that precautions may be necessary unless specifically advised, and she had made no attempt. If the truth were known, she hadn't even though about it. The emotions he had aroused in her had been too intense, too immediate to leave room for practicalities.

Now, almost two months later, she wasn't even sure how she felt about him anymore. No fire lasted without fuel to feed it. She knew where the DuTemple estate was—she had even driven past it on occasion—but in all these weeks she had never once laid eyes on him. Whatever his plans for the future, the marriage had not yet taken place: the DuTemple name alone would have elicited attention by the media. Remembering that last night on Royale, Vanessa felt her throat muscles contract. The pain had been real enough then, there was no doubt.

She made herself move to fetch the tray from the patio. None of this introspection was helping. It was the future she had to look to not the past. One parent families were no rarity these days, and she was fortunate enough to be in a position where money was no immediate problem. She could be thankful now that her father had managed to persuade her to leave her capital where it was. If she could just work out what to do about her share in the boat everything would be fine.

She broached the subject when Brenden came to supper that evening, but he remained adamant in his refusal to accept her half as a gift.

'I'd buy her from you if I could,' he conceded gruffly. 'By rights she should be yours anyway.'

A debatable point, Vanessa reflected, considering the way she had been acquired. Irrelevant right now though, she had to admit. 'Dad thought a lot of you,' she said. 'He just didn't give enough thought to what he was doing when he drew up that will of his.'

'If you stayed on in Caledonia there wouldn't be any problem,' Brenden pointed out. 'Especially as Neal's buried here.'

'I know you'll take care of the grave for me.' Vanessa had no intention of telling him why she had to go. 'We'll just have to let the banks handle the financial arrangements,' she added.

'I suppose so.' He sounded despondent. 'I'm going to miss you, Van. You *and* Neal.' He glanced at the wall clock, stirring reluctantly. 'I'd better go. I've an early start. Sure you won't come out with us?'

'No thanks.' Her voice was soft. 'It wouldn't be the same.'

'True.' Impulsively he leaned forward to kiss her cheek. 'See you tomorrow night.'

He would be fine, Vanessa reassured herself, carrying the supper dishes through to the kitchen. He'd already proved himself more than capable of handling things on his own, although he was still on the look out for a suitable first-mate. Good crewmen were hard to come by; there were too many drifters. It was difficult to remember that Brenden had been one of them once.

The knock on the outer door startled her for a moment. Something he must have forgotten, she surmised, going to answer it. Her breath died on her when she saw the man waiting on the stone step. She could only stand there gazing at him helplessly.

Raoul was the first to speak, voice cool and level. 'Are you going to invite me inside, or must we talk on the step?'

Still mute, Vanessa stood back to allow him entry, closing the door with care before turning to face him. 'The living room is through there,' she said with what coolness of her own she could muster. 'Would you like some coffee?'

He made no answer, moving ahead of her into the room to cast a comprehensive glance around. She steeled herself to meet the blue eyes, reading disdain into his appraisal and feeling her pride rise to the occasion. He had found her desirable once.

'Pierre tells me you're pregnant,' he said bluntly. 'Is it true?'

'He had no right,' she protested. 'A doctor is supposed to respect the confidences . . .'

'You're not his patient.' The interruption was abrupt. 'And that's no answer.'

She drew a steadying breath. 'Yes, it's true. He made the diagnosis himself.'

'And you claim the child is mine?'

Her body tensed again. 'Your name wasn't mentioned!'

'Seven or eight weeks, you told Pierre. More subtle than a direct accusation, I agree, but no less damaging. Seven weeks ago you were with me on Royale. He knew that as well as anyone.' He paused, regard hard and unyielding. 'It was no virgin I took that time on the beach. You'd known men before me.'

'One man.' The denial was dragged from her. 'I only ever slept with one man before you. We were going to be married.'

'But not anymore?'

'No. I wrote and told him I'd be staying here with my father. He never replied to the letter.'

'Was that before or after you came to Royale?'

Vanessa hesitated, seeing the pitfalls. 'Actually it was while I was there. I gave it to one of the staff to post for me here on the mainland.' She made a small defensive gesture. 'It hardly matters, does it. I'm not asking you for anything. You wouldn't even have known about it if Doctor Renaud hadn't given me a lift home from the cemetery. And you were the one who asked him to come, remember.'

Raoul ignored the outburst. 'You were here in Caledonia only a week before we met again. How can you be certain that the child wasn't conceived before you left England?'

Vanessa flushed, not because of what she was about to say but because of what would surely follow. 'I was taking precautions then.'

Dark brows lifted sardonically. 'But not since?'

'There was no reason to suppose I was going to need a new prescription.' She was fighting to stay reasonable about it. 'I didn't plan on getting into bed with anyone while I was away. You were . . . it all happened so fast.'

'So quickly it never once occurred to you to warn me of the risks we were running?'

'No.' She paused. 'I never even thought about it. Can you really believe I wanted this to happen?'

'Why not?' His tone bit. 'I'd hardly be the first man to be caught in such a trap.'

White hot anger seared through her. She pointed a trembling finger at the door. 'Get out!'

'I'll go,' he said, 'when I'm ready to go. There are things we have to talk about first.'

'Such as what?' she flung at him. 'I'm not getting rid of it, if that's what you're going to suggest!'

'There's no question of that,' he responded on the same hard note. 'Tomorrow you'll see a gynaecologist.'

'And if I refuse?'

He shook his head. 'You won't refuse. I won't allow you to refuse. The ceremony will take place as soon as possible.'

'Ceremony?' Green eyes had widened in shock. 'I don't . . .'

'No child of mine will be born without a name.'

She stared at him, mind too confused for rational thought. 'A moment ago you weren't even convinced it *was* your child.'

His expression altered. 'You're telling me now there may be some doubt?'

'No' she said hollowly. 'No there isn't any doubt. That doesn't mean I'm willing to marry you.' She groped for a seat, holding up a staying hand as he started towards her. 'Just leave me alone!'

'You're feeling sick again?' he demanded.

'No,' Vanessa said again. 'That only happens up until around lunchtime.' Her laugh jarred. 'If the funeral had been this afternoon instead of this morning there'd have been no problem!'

Raoul's expression was uncertain. 'You'd have left without telling anyone?'

'That was the plan, although I wasn't sure where I was going to go.' She added thickly, 'You don't have to concern yourself. I can cope quite adequately. Ante-natal care is free in England.'

'You're not going to England,' he said roughly. 'Not with my son.'

A curious sensation stirred in her. 'What makes you so sure it will be a boy?'

'There have been only two females born to the line in more than two hundred years.'

'I suppose that would shorten the odds.' She made a valiant effort to rally her forces. 'You can't make me stay here, even so.'

He was looking at her as if he found it difficult to believe what he was hearing. 'You'd rob him of his future?'

'He'll have a future. Not quite the same kind, of course, but at least he'll never be made to feel he got it by default!'

'There's no question of laying any blame at a child's door!'

'You've done just that where your father's other two sons are concerned, haven't you?' she retorted, and saw the lean features darken anew.

'I have no intention of trying to justify myself in that direction. If you force me I'll take legal action to have you detained.'

'You can hardly have an unborn baby made a ward of court, if that's the kind of thing you're thinking of. You don't have any jurisdiction, Raoul.'

'This is French territory not British,' he said. 'How would you know the way the law stands here?'

She didn't, she was bound to admit. Yet the alternative held little appeal either. What kind of future would a loveless marriage offer a child? Better than the one she had mapped out, came the unwilling thought. Boy or girl, a child needed a father. She knew that better than anyone. There was also the question of birthright. If she fought Raoul's claim she would be putting her own interests first. Could she live with that knowledge?

'What about Crystal?' she asked desperately, still looking for a way out.

Raoul's tone was unrevealing. 'What about her?'

'You were going to be married.' She glanced up at him when he made no immediate answer, surprising an expression in the blue eyes that prompted her to add slowly, 'At least, that's what she told me.'

He studied her for a long moment before replying. 'You'd be willing to hand over the child for adoption when the time came.'

'To you and her?' The rejection was fierce. 'No way!'

The veil dropped again. 'Then we have no alternative. Naturally, the ceremony will be a quiet one, and within the next two or three days. In the meantime, I want your passport.'

Vanessa gritted her teeth. 'I'm not going to run away.'

'You wouldn't get far if you tried, but that isn't the reason.' His smile came briefly and without humour. 'There are times when one's use of a word is out of context. I should have said I *need* your passport—for official purposes. Will you get it for me please.'

She fetched it without further protest, handing it over with a sense of burning her boats behind her. His closeness stirred memories she preferred to forget, jerking words from her.

'It won't work, Raoul. It can't work! We don't have any basis to build on.'

There was no softening of purpose in him. 'Then we make one.'

'From what?'

'From what we had in the past.'

'That was over the day you left Royale.'

'No,' he said, 'it wasn't over. We simply put it aside. It seemed the best way at the time.' His tone briskened. 'I'll make the appointment for the afternoon. Naturally, I'll be accompanying you. Can you be ready for two o'clock?'

Vanessa nodded, not trusting her voice. He would want confirmation before he went ahead with any further arrangements; she couldn't blame him for that. He was ready to sacrifice his freedom of choice in order to protect the life she carried within her. Could she do less?

Only when he had gone and she was alone again did she try to rationalise her emotions. There was something there still between them, she was forced to acknowledge that, but could the spark be rekindled? Even if it could it was hardly going to be enough to carry them through the coming years. Yet it was possible for love to grow between two people given time and opportunity. Perhaps not the all-consuming kind one read about, but did that really exist anyway? They would have a child to build their lives around, perhaps even more than one. Why not let matters take their course and stop clutching at the might-have-beens.

*   *   *

They were married by civil ceremony, with only the necessary witnesses in attendance. Vanessa wore a cream silk suit and matching, wide-brimmed hat, but carried no flowers. Her only adornment lay in the single string of superbly matched pearls Raoul had given her for a wedding present. She hadn't wanted to accept them, but he had insisted; the same way he had insisted she also accept the square-cut emerald ring. Keeping up appearances, she had told herself cynically. The quietness and secrecy of the wedding arrangements would no doubt excite their own comment, but the bride would at least be properly decked.

Afterwards, sitting silently by his side in the car as they headed for the home she had not yet seen from the inside, she went back over the past few days in her mind. There had been so much to do, so much to think about. The gynaecologist Raoul had arranged for her to see had been reassuring in his assessment. Her health was excellent, her pregnancy progressing along standard lines. The baby would be born at the end of February. Her real problem lay in her mental attitude; she still felt so little involvement. Perhaps once there was some more definite physical evidence it would be different.

Visualising the way she was going to look in another couple of months, she wondered how Raoul might react. What attraction she still held for him was hardly going to be enhanced by a steadily thickening figure. There was no tenderness to carry them through, no shared delight in this being they had created. They were two people brought together by circumstance, nothing else.

'Are you feeling all right?' he asked suddenly, jerking her out of her reverie. 'Do you want me to stop the car?'

Vanessa shook her head. 'No, I'm fine. Just a little nervous, that's all.'

He gave her a quizzical glance. 'Of me?'

'Of everything,' she admitted. 'Do they know at the house that you're bringing back a wife this afternoon?'

'Naturally they know. There were preperations to be made. I had the master suite opened up. It hasn't been used since my stepmother left. You may want to have it redecorated before moving in.'

'I'm sure that won't be necessary,' she said. She paused before adding on a tentative note, 'Will anyone else be there?'

'If you mean Crystal, she left yesterday.' His tone was quite unemotional.

Until that moment she had refused to acknowledge how much she had dreaded the encounter, yet her relief was tempered by the swift surge of guilt. 'She must hate me,' she said impulsively.

'Yes, I think she does.' There was still no particular inflection. 'She'll get over it.'

Would he? she thought with a pang. 'I really messed things up, didn't I?' she murmured.

He smiled faintly. 'We both did that. It will teach me never to take anything for granted. It isn't an ideal way to start a marriage, but if we both put our minds to it we can make something worthwhile.'

What about hearts? she wanted to ask, only the words wouldn't come. His heart didn't enter into it. It probably never would.

CHAPTER SEVEN

THE DuTemple residence lay within its own grounds some three miles outside the town limits. From the wrought iron gates, it was a quarter of a mile to the house itself, the wide drive running straight as a die between a double row of causerinas. Massed flowerbeds intersected the stretches of lawn beyond.

'It's just like Royale!' Vanessa exclaimed, viewing the long pillared frontage, sparkling white in the afternoon sunshine. 'Only larger, of course.'

'Grandfather was a man of limited imagination,' Raoul agreed. 'He copied the design because he couldn't visualise anything better. 'At least you'll have no difficulty in finding your way around. The interior layout follows the same pattern too.' He drew the car to a halt before the imposing entrance portal and switched off the engine, sitting for a moment with his hands resting on the wheel as he studied her face. 'Still feeling nervous?'

'Yes,' she admitted. 'I can't help it. You've been used to this all your life. I don't even speak the language with any fluency.'

'All it takes is time and practice. A few months from now you'll wonder why you ever found it difficult.' He got out of the car as a stocky Polynesian in a white jacket appeared from the house, coming round to open her door while the man gathered up her belongings from the boot. 'This is Kehei,' he said. 'He and his wife Kalani have charge of the household staff.'

Vanessa murmured a greeting to the man, cheered

by his wide white smile. If his wife was as friendly life wouldn't be so bad. They entered the house to find her waiting for them in the beautifully proportioned hall, as fat as a tub of lard and totally lacking in servility. They could have tea any time they were ready, she declared.

'A concession to your English habits,' Raoul observed as they mounted the stairs. 'You won't go far wrong if you put yourself in Kalani's hands. She already had three children of her own, although they're all grown-up now and gone.'

'She knows about the baby?' Vanessa asked.

'Of course. It would have become all too obvious in a few weeks, in any case.' A smile touched his mouth. 'She's delighted. For years she's been telling me I should have a son to carry on the name. The Tahitians love all children.'

'Supposing it isn't a boy?' she ventured. 'There has to be a chance, no matter how remote.'

'Then we simply try again.' He glanced her way, expression suddenly firming. 'Time is on our side.'

They had reached the top of the staircase. Raoul turned right along the shorter arm of the open gallery, opening a door of solid polished mahogany to usher her through ahead of him. Vanessa found herself in a large and lovely sitting room decorated in pale greens and white. Thick carpeting the colour of rich moss sprang underfoot. There were french windows in the rear wall, giving on to a wide balcony with a superb view out to sea. Through a further door lay the bedroom, sharing the same balcony and view, and beyond that again a beautifully appointed bathroom with sunken bath and mirrored walls. The whole suite was as big as a small house in area.

Kehei brought up her baggage while she was still in

the process of inspection, leaving it in the bedroom at her request. Raoul came through as she opened up her suitcase. He had taken off the jacket of his formal suit and was unbuttoning his shirt.

'Kalani will unpack for you,' he said. 'Just take out what you need for now and leave the rest.'

'I'd rather do it myself,' she claimed truthfully, head bent to her task. 'I'm not used to being waited on hand and foot.'

'Unlike my stepmama who demanded it.' He watched her for a moment before adding curiously, 'Is this all you have, or is there more to come?'

'It's all I have here,' she said. 'I left a few things in storage back home, but I never bothered sending for them because I wasn't sure what was going to happen after Dad went.' She tried to say it matter-of-factly but didn't quite succeed. 'The house was sold fully furnished so it doesn't amount to much. Just a few mementos. Most of the clothes I left behind are winter wear. I don't suppose they're going to be much use out here.'

'No,' he agreed. 'Noumea has several excellent salons. You must outfit yourself anew.'

'Befitting my status?'

'If that's the way you want to see it.' There was a pause, a sudden sigh. When he spoke again his tone was gentler. 'Vanessa, come here.'

She stiffened despite herself. 'Why?'

He moved then, coming across to turn her towards him. The white silk shirt was hanging free of his waistband, baring the breadth of his chest. She had a sudden flaring urge to press her lips into the crisply curling hair, a need to feel his hands seize her, hold her close against his hardness. The past weeks had only dulled the memories not erased them. She had never stopped wanting him, she knew that now.

Whatever he had been about to say died on his lips as she lifted darkened green eyes. When he kissed her it was as if he couldn't help himself. She responded with a kind of desperation, going up on her toes to reach him, rediscovering the feel of the muscular body. If they had nothing else they could still have this. It was enough for now. It had to be enough.

She trembled to the touch of his hands when he removed her suit top and the scanty lace garment beneath, her breasts springing eagerly into his seeking fingers. They were fuller than before, the aureolas already beginning to darken from their virgin pink, the nipples to enlarge. She heard him catch his breath as he looked, then he was bending his head and his tongue was tasting her, teasing her, driving her insane with its flickering torment. Her hands fastened in his hair, clutching him to her, reluctant to let go even when he slid an arm beneath her knees and lifted her bodily from the floor.

'I never made love to a pregnant woman before,' he murmered thickly. 'You must tell me if I hurt you.'

The bed felt yielding, the satin cover smooth and cool to her skin. He finished undressing her without undue haste, pausing to trace the barely discernible rounding of her belly with fingers so gentle she could scarcely feel them. She sensed his intrigue with her altered shape, the beginning of wonder. He had planted the seed from which the being inside her had sprung—the ultimate proof of his male virility. He may never love her but he would love their child. There was nothing surer.

'I'm going to be ugly,' she whispered, unable to keep her doubts and fears hidden. 'You won't want to look at me soon.'

'Not true,' he denied, lips warm against her skin. 'The mother of my son could never be ugly to me.'

Was it possible, Vanessa wondered hollowly, to feel jealous of one's own unborn child? Was that her whole problem perhaps? She didn't want to believe herself capable of such an emotion. Not for the first time she wished she could only turn back the clock. Yet would it make any real difference in the long run? She was as likely to make the same mistakes. Raoul had only to touch her the way he was doing now to have her melting beneath him, her thighs parting to his demand. She had no will of her own, only desire, rising in her like a floodtide to obliterate the world.

Life settled into a pattern of sorts over the following few days. In the mornings they swam together in the oval pool beneath their balcony, then lay in the sun for an hour talking desultorily until coffee was brought to them. Later they might drive along the coast to take lunch in one of the small inns tucked away among the palm trees, or simply to view the scenery of this lazy, lovely fragment of France. Vanessa lived for the moment, blanking out all thoughts of the future. What happened would happen; she could only accept.

'I have a board meeting tomorrow,' Raoul stated over dinner one evening towards the end of that first week. 'Unfortunately my commitments won't wait any longer.'

He sounded distinctly regretful. Enough so, at least, to temper Vanessa's initial despondency. 'It was good of you to take so much time to spend with me,' she said with a formality that drew a faint smile to his lips.

'The least I could do under the circumstances. I wish now that I'd taken you away from Caledonia altogether.'

'A proper honeymoon, you mean?' She kept her tone light. 'Hardly appropriate *under* the circumstances.'

He studied her a moment, then shrugged. 'Perhaps not. Later, after he's born, we can think about it again.' The blue eyes narrowed as her expression went blank. 'Something in you closes against me every time I mention the event,' he observed dispassionately. 'Does the thought of giving birth bother you?'

'The thought of not giving birth to the son you've set your heart on does,' she prevaricated. 'You're going to be so terribly disappointed if it turns out to be a girl after all.'

'Disappointed perhaps, but not inconsolable. The chances would be even greater the next time.'

'Assuming there'd be a next time.'

'What we did once we can surely do again—unless you intend denying me my conjugal rights.'

She said softly, 'Are you likely to let me?'

'Not unless you could convince me that my attentions were no longer desirable to you.' His tone gentled a little. 'It may be all we have now but it needn't stay that way. We have a lot of tastes in common, Vanessa. More than I realised. The days we spent together on Royale were too physically orientated to allow time for getting to know each other on any other level. Do you understand what I'm trying to say?'

Her eyes were on the brandy glass cupped between the lean brown hands. 'Yes.'

There was a pause before he spoke again, voice expressionless. 'It's time you began meeting some people. Do you feel up to coping with a dinner party?'

Panic caught her by the throat. 'Must I?'

'I can't force you,' he said. 'I wouldn't even try. Do you prefer the life of a recluse?'

I have you, she wanted to say, that's enough. She bit it back because it was too soon, too emotional, too lacking in plausibility. 'They'll all know,' she said instead. 'If they don't they'll suspect. No one gets married as quickly and secretly as we did without reason.'

'Most men would prefer a similiar lack of ceremony if given a choice,' Raoul retorted drily. 'The speculation would have been no less had we invited the whole of Noumea.'

'Because everyone took it for granted you were going to marry Crystal?'

He sat cradling the glass for a moment or two more before answering, regard steady. 'The thought still upsets you?'

She said huskily, 'It makes me feel guilty.'

'If there's any guilt to be felt we share it equally.'

'Then it was true?'

He sighed. 'Yes, it was true. Now can we please forget it. I asked you a question. Can you cope?'

Vanessa made a supreme effort. 'I expect so. If I have to do it at all I suppose it's better now while I'm still able to squeeze into something half decent.'

'That's another thing,' Raoul said. 'You're going to need a complete new wardrobe. Simone Renaud would be only too pleased to accompany you on a shopping expedition. She's been asking to meet you. You'd find a friend in her if in no one else.'

Vanessa glanced at him swiftly. 'You never mentioned her before.'

'I was waiting for the right opportunity. Kehei could take you into town tomorrow and pick up Simone on the way. They live not far from the clinic. Afterwards the two of you can meet me for lunch. Agreed?'

There was no point in disagreeing. He was right, she couldn't shut herself away. Pierre Renaud's wife had to be nice—and she was already a mother. Perhaps from her she could learn what it really meant.

It was only later when Raoul was breathing evenly and deeply at her side in the bed that she allowed herself to think about Crystal again. Raoul didn't give the appearance of a man thwarted in love, yet for what other reason would he have contemplated the marriage at all? She had never even seen him with his stepsister. How could she begin to guess what his feelings might be? If he had put the interests of their child before his own then she could do no less.

Simone Renaud was in her early thirties, slender and attractive with her gamine features and close-fitting cap of dark hair. She had twin daughters aged eighteen months and a son of four years already to her credit, and made no secret of a desire for more.

'I was one of six,' she confided when they were in the car together, having left the children in the care of their nanny. 'Pierre holds up his hands in horror at the thought, but he's only pretending. Men are enchanted by their own progeny.'

'Even when they're unsolicited?' The words were out before Vanessa could stop them, torn from a place deep down inside her where the pain and doubt still lurked. She flushed at Simone's swift glance, thankful for the glass partition cutting the two of them off from Kehei up front. 'Forget I said that,' she added huskily. 'It was wrong of me.'

'If something troubles you it's better out than in,' came the soft reply. 'I think I can understand the way you must feel, Vanessa, but Raoul is a good man for all his faults. He won't let you down.'

'It isn't that I'm afraid of,' Vanessa confessed,

drawn despite herself by the sympathetic tone. 'He'll stick by me for the baby's sake.'

'Only you need more than that.' It was statement not a question. There was a momentary pause before Simone added on the same soft note, 'Do you love him?'

Her shrug was almost defensive. 'I barely know him.'

'It isn't necessary to know a man to love him. We women follow our hearts not our heads. You must have some feeling for him to have married him at all.'

'You don't think being pregnant by him is enough?'

'Not in this day and age. There's little stigma attached. It would have been relatively simple for you to have got rid of the child had you been concerned only with that aspect.'

'I don't believe in abortion,' Vanessa rejoined. 'Not in these circumstances, at any rate. And I could never have provided the kind of lifestyle Raoul will provide.'

'There's more to life than the material things. However, I agree a child should have two parents if at all possible.' Simone studied her thoughtfully. 'Speaking as a friend, I think Raoul should consider himself fortunate. Not only does he have what he most wanted and needed in the world, but in you he has a wife who will do him credit. I know because I'm a good judge of character. Crystal wouldn't have made him happy. She is like her name, beautiful but brittle. She promised him a child, yet she'd have prevaricated when it came to the point.'

Vanessa said slowly, 'You're saying he only wanted to marry her because of that?'

'Who knows? Men are like babes themselves when it comes to seeing through a beautiful woman. For Pierre she could do no wrong. For me . . .' She paused, mouth twisting a little. 'Suffice to say she's not a woman's woman, and never could be. She wouldn't be interested. From the time she was old enough to think about marriage she was determined to have Raoul for herself. If he had been as certain they would have been man and wife long before you arrived on the scene. Jules wanted it, even though his marriage to her mother wasn't a success.'

Jules had wanted it but Raoul himself had not been certain. Vanessa clung to that thought.

They were coming into the Place des Cocotiers, shaded by its magnificent flame trees. Faded pink stone buildings stood cheek by jowl with modern structures of glass and concrete. Kehei dropped them off close by the chic boutiques full of ready-mades from all the great fashion houses of France, arranging to pick them up again at noon to take them to their luncheon date with Raoul.

'That gives us almost three hours to do what we have to do,' said Simone, leading the way. 'It will barely be enough.'

Vanessa began to see what she meant during the following hour as garment after garment was brought to the fitting room for their approval. The fuller maternity wear could wait, the Frenchwoman declared with authority. For now what was needed were the simple flowing lines which would conceal an expanding waistline without appearing to do so. She kept on one dress in pale amber linen because her own cotton suit was already tight around the middle, content to allow Simone to make the arrangements for delivery of the rest. Afterwards it was shoes and sandals in finest leather by Cardin and Martin and Jourdan, with handbags and purses to match, silver and gold evening slippers to go with the two long dresses already purchased. One could never have too many pairs of shoes, was Simone's surprised answer when Vanessa attempted at one point to restrain her enthusiasm. Raoul would not anticipate that any budget be adhered to—might even consider any frugality on her part as a slur on his ability to provide. She was married to one of the island's elite, and must learn to act the part. Vanessa doubted that she ever would, but felt bound to make the effort. It wasn't exactly a penance she was being asked to pay, she told herself wryly.

Raoul was already waiting for them in the old colonial building which housed one of Noumea's finest restaurants. He was wearing a suit in dark blue tropical worsted which Vanessa hadn't seen before. The blue eyes rested in unconcealed approval on the amber dress.

'A good choice,' he declared. 'It suits your colouring.'

And was worthy of his standing in the eyes of those even now casting sly glances in their direction, came the wry thought as they moved to their seats. The dinner party he had spoken of last night was going to tax her resources to the limit, but it had to be gone through. Simone would help if asked, she was certain, yet it would be a feather in her cap if she could manage it on her own. It wasn't as if she had to do the actual cooking herself.

The meal was superb. Vanessa had fish clothed in flaky pastry, and enjoyed every mouthful.

'I've eaten too much,' she confessed in the end, laying down her fork with reluctance. 'It's so delicious!'

'You're eating for two,' Simone responded easily. 'That makes it all right. I put on too many kilos with Christian, but it all disappeared afterwards. Shall you breast-feed?'

Vanessa avoided glancing in Raoul's direction. 'I hadn't thought about it yet.'

'Then you should. It's by far the best. There's no truth in the notion that it spoils the figure.' She laughed. 'Pierre would have been the first to complain!'

'Since when did Pierre dare to complain?' asked Raoul on a light note, drawing a look of mock outrage.

'You make me sound so terrible a woman! Don't listen to him, Vanessa.'

'I wouldn't believe it, anyway,' Vanessa assured her, smiling a little. 'Pierre doesn't exactly look downtrodden.' This time she met Raoul's gaze. 'About this dinner party. Who do I invite?'

'A party?' Simone sounded interested. 'Whose idea was that?'

'Mine,' Raoul claimed. 'Naturally, you and Pierre would be top of the list.'

'Naturally.' She was looking at Vanessa. 'Do you feel up to it?'

The same question Raoul himself had asked, though with rather different inflection. Vanessa smiled again and made the same answer. 'If I don't now I'm unlikely to later. The sooner people have their curiosity satisfied the better, I suppose.'

'There's no obligation,' Raoul said softly. 'I already told you that.'

Green eyes remained level. 'And I already said I'd do it. All I want is some help with the names.'

'Which I can provide,' put in Simone quickly. 'We will make a list of possibles. I think no more than ten people, including yourselves—yes?'

'You're the expert.' Raoul sounded as if he couldn't really care less one way or the other. 'I'm sure Vanessa will be content to leave it in your hands. Would you like dessert?'

She'd show him, Vanessa thought on a surge of sudden and unwonted rage. She would show them all!

If Simone had recognised the change of mood she made no mention of it during the drive home. Vanessa accepted her invitation to come in and see a little more of the children because it would have seemed churlish to refuse. They were an enchanting trio, she was bound to acknowledge, the boy, Christian, a miniature replica of his father. Although her French was improved, she still found difficulty in following some of the child's quick prattle, much to his amusement. Vanessa laughed with him at her mistakes, ruefully confiding to Simone later over tea her doubt that she would ever be proficient in the language.

'It will come,' the other assured her. 'One can't live in a French speaking community and fail to pick up the language eventually. Raoul could help by insisting that you speak French when you're together. It's frustrating, I know, in the beginning, but it's by far the best way.'

Pierre had said much the same thing once, Vanessa recalled. How long ago it seemed now. She had a sudden yearning to be back on the island—back where it had all started. Yet it could hardly be the same, could it? They no longer had that freedom of choice.

'I'd give anything not to be having this baby,' she said, and only realised she had spoken her thoughts aloud when she saw Simone's expression alter.

'You don't really mean that,' said the Frenchwoman with some authority. 'If you feel little for it now, you will once you hold it in your arms. You have to stop resenting the way things are, Vanessa. Give your marriage a chance to succeed.'

She was right, of course. Vanessa summoned a wry smile. 'I'll do my best.' Deliberately she changed the subject. 'How about making up that list? I'd like to get the invitations out as soon as possible. I suppose I'd better do it formally considering I don't know any of the people concerned.'

It was gone four-thirty when she finally left the Renaud residence. Raoul had already returned and was taking a shower when she reached their suite. He came through to the bathroom door with a towel wrapped about lean hips while she was still sorting through the boxes that had been delivered during the afternoon from the boutique in Nouméa, using a second towel to rub his hair dry.

'You managed to find everything you needed?' he asked, looking at the piled packages.

'Enough for three,' Vanessa returned, still feeling guilty at the thought of what it must all have cost. 'Simone wouldn't let me look at any prices, so I couldn't begin to say how much the bill is going to come to.'

Dark brows lifted a fraction. 'I never knew a woman who worried about that particular aspect before.'

'You never knew one like me before,' she said, and saw him smile suddenly and fleetingly.

'True. You're a constant source of surprise.'

She watched him as he dropped the towel he had been using on his hair to the floor behind him, feeling her pulses leap as he lifted a casual hand to his head to rake through the damp thickness. His body was so taut and fit, the muscularity defined without overstatement. She knew the tempered steel of those arms, the driving power in his loins—knew, and wanted. The same blind instinct that had got her into this predicament in the first place, she reminded herself with irony, and not to be confused with love.

He knew what was going through her mind; she

could see that in his eyes when she lifted her glance back to his face. She restrained the impulse to back off as he moved slowly towards her. Denying her need fooled neither of them.

The towel slid from his hips as he kissed her. He made no attempt to catch it, turning her round to face the long mirrored doors fronting the wall of wardrobes. Vanessa stood still in his light grasp as he gently slid the zip on the amber dress and eased it over her shoulders. She saw his head bend, felt the touch of his lips at her nape, soft as a butterfly's wings brushing her skin. In another man it might have been tenderness; with Raoul, she thought cynically, it was simply technique. He knew so well how to reach a woman, how to build the desire in her until her whole body craved fulfilment. His mouth was moving now, slowly, oh so slowly, leaving a trail of fire in its wake, his fingers curving to cup the fullness of her breasts before smoothing a path downwards over hip and flank, drawing her up against him as they sought the very centre of her being. The familiar drumming was in her ears, catching her up in its beat until she no longer knew who or what or where she was, only that she existed.

Darkness had long fallen before Raoul stirred himself to glance at the time.

'We should get ready for dinner,' he murmured, subsiding back into the pillows. 'Unless you'd prefer to have it brought up here?'

Vanessa hadn't moved; she felt both satiated and momentarily secure. 'Would it be a lot of trouble?'

He laughed. 'Not for us. Not for Kalani either, if it comes to that. She approves of you, Vanessa. Not an accolade she extends to everyone, believe me. My stepmother was always at war with her.'

'You didn't like her very much either, did you?' Vanessa said softly. 'Your stepmother, I mean.'

There was a pause before he answered, the intonation flat. 'She was a very self-centred woman—still is, if it comes to that. I was at an age where it would have taken someone of very special qualities to take the place of my own mother. I could never understand how my father could have brought himself to marry her at all. Looking back now, I think he may have been swayed as much by the desire to provide her child with a real home. He had a very great regard for Crystal.'

'That didn't make you jealous?'

'Of a five year old girl? No, I wasn't jealous. I was still his only son then.'

There was a risk, a very great risk entailed in taking the allusion any further, but Vanessa had to ask. 'Did Elise die?'

This time the pause was longer. 'Yes,' he admitted at length. 'The boys are in a good home with a family who care about them. They don't know about me, and I don't want to know about them—except for making sure they're never in any need. I set up a trust for the two of them. That's as far as I'm prepared to go.'

'I understand,' she said. 'I really do.'

'Yes, I think you do.' He rolled on to his side, coming up on an elbow to look at her, expression relaxing. 'I have a lot to be thankful for.'

'Me too.' Her voice sounded husky. In that moment she was closer to loving him than she had ever been. 'Some men would have left me flat.'

He grinned suddenly, placing a hand lightly across her abdomen, fingers spread to accommodate the curvature. 'Hardly flat.'

'A figure of speech.' Her senses were coming alive

again, yet there was no displacing the tight little band about her chest. The only hold she had over him was right there under his hand; without it she was nothing.

CHAPTER EIGHT

IT was the middle of the following week before Vanessa could bring herself to pay Brenden a visit. She found him swabbing down the deck after a morning charter, sun-bronzed and fit in his cut-off jeans and faded cotton vest.

'I was beginning to think I wasn't going to see you again,' he admitted when they were below with a mug of coffee apiece. 'That note you sent me was a real shock.'

'I was too much of a coward to tell you to your face,' Vanessa acknowledged wryly. 'Especially after losing Dad. Don't think too badly of me, Bren.'

'I don't think badly of you at all,' he denied. 'It could happen to anybody. The only thing that bothers me is whether you're happy or not.' He eyed her for a moment as if seeking the answer in her face. 'Are you?'

'Of course. It's just taking a bit of getting used to, that's all.' She smiled a little. 'I can think of a whole lot of people who'd envy me the opportunity. Most women dream of a rich husband.'

'I'll bet you were never one of them, though,' he came back shrewdly. 'In fact, I'd say the money was the least part of it. He's lucky to have got you. I hope he realises it.'

'He isn't complaining.' She made an effort to change the subject. 'How are things going with you?'

'Couldn't be better. As much work as I can handle.'

'You didn't find a mate yet?'

'Not a permanent one, no. There's no real

necessity.' He was getting to his feet. 'I'll show you
the accounts.'

'I don't want to see them,' she denied. 'It isn't why
I came.'

'It's still your business. Half of it, at any rate.' He
extracted a quarto-sized account book from a shelf and
opened it at the page in use, holding it out to her
stubbornly. 'You have to take an interest, Van. It's
what Neal wanted. I've opened a special account with
the bank for your share of the profit. Whether you use
it or not, it's going to keep going in.'

'All right.' At that particular moment she could see
no way round the problem. Ethically, they neither of
them had any claim to the boat, but there was little to
be done about it. Certainly Raoul would have no
interest in acquiring it for his own use. 'I'll leave it to
accumulate.'

It didn't satify him, she could see that, but he let it
lie. 'How about a run out on the lagoon?' he asked. 'I
don't have anything else on this afternoon.'

She shook her head regretfully. 'I don't have the
time. I told Kehei to come back for me at four.'

'Supposing I hadn't been here?'

'I'd have had a long wait. I wasn't going to walk all
the way down here first to find out.' She drained her
coffee mug and set it down, pressing herself to her
feet. 'Maybe next time.'

'So let's make it a date,' he insisted. 'I'll keep Friday
free. Some sea air would do you good. You don't have
a lot of colour in your cheeks.' His tone softened in
persuasion. 'I've missed you this last couple of weeks.
Both of you. There aren't going to be all that many
more opportunities, I imagine.'

Before she got too big and clumsy? Vanessa
reflected drily. It was a point. She knew he hadn't

meant that. Not in the same way. She missed former
times too.

'It will have to be in the morning,' she said. 'We
have a dinner party Friday evening.'

'In your condition?' Brenden caught himself up,
flushing a little. 'I was just thinking it would be a bit
of a strain, that's all.'

A bit was an understatement, but there was no point
in letting him know that. 'I'll cope,' she said. 'It's not
ten weeks yet.'

'But it's common knowledge.'

Vanessa winced despite herself. 'It would have to
be, wouldn't it? In a place the size of Noumea there
could never be any secrets. I suppose the general
consensus of opinion is that I trapped Raoul into the
situation.'

'The general consensus down here seems to be that
he at least had the decency to do the right thing by
you,' came the surprising reply. 'You were one of us
for a while. You made some friends along the wharfs.'

'I did?' She was gratified, and oddly comforted.
'That helps.'

'So you'll definitely come back Friday?'

'I'll try,' she promised. 'That's the best I can say. If
you're offered a charter between now and then, take it.'

Kehei was leaning against the car when she reached
the wharf, his expression that of a man who could find
better things to do with his time.

'I've jobs to do back at the house,' he grumbled, low
toned as he put the vehicle into gear. 'I ain't no
chauffeur.'

It would make life easier for both of them, Vanessa
conceded, if she had her own transport. Perhaps she
could suggest it to Raoul. There was no reason why he
should object. A measure of independence was what

she needed, even if only to prove she was still her own person.

In the end it was Raoul who raised the subject himself over coffee on the terrace that evening.

'I think it might be a good idea if you had a car of your own,' he said quietly enough. 'Only not to keep going down to the *Julia*. I'd rather you stayed away from there, Vanessa.'

'I can't just stop seeing Brenden altogether,' she pointed out, trying to sound reasonable about it. 'He did a lot for my father.' She hesitated before going on. 'Dad left equal shares in the boat to the two of us. I realise it could be considered that it wasn't his to leave in the first place, but that's the way it is. What I'd really like is for Brenden to have the lot, only he won't take it. Perhaps you have a solution.'

'It isn't my problem.' Raoul's tone was brusque. 'No matter how I might have felt about the way he obtained it, the boat was your father's to do as he liked with. If it's what you want, just have the papers made over legally to Hartley. He can hardly refuse an accomplished fact.'

It was one way, Vanessa was bound to concede, if not exactly satisfactory. It would be like closing the last door on her past life. Not a bad thing perhaps, considering the mess she had made of it. For the first time in weeks she thought of Michael, wondering what he was doing with himself. He had never replied to her letter, but then why should he? She had made it plain that there was no hope for the future.

'I still didn't do anything about transferring the money I got for the house in England,' she said diffidently. 'It should come to around eighty-thousand pounds with interest.'

'The company lawyers can take care of the

transaction, and handle the investment for you.'

'For me.'

'Of course. The days when a woman's properties automatically became her husband's are long gone.'

'Then I'll hardly need the allowance you settled on me.'

Blue eyes hardened a fraction. 'Are you suggesting I should let my wife buy her own clothes?'

'No. Well, not exactly that. I . . .' She broke off, already regretting the unstudied remark. 'I'm not used to having so much, I suppose.'

It was a moment before Raoul spoke again. When he did it was with an odd inflection. 'What kind of life would you have led if you'd married the man you left in England?'

Vanessa glanced at him swiftly and away again, remembering what he knew of that relationship. 'A whole lot different from this. He's a sales representative in electrical components.'

'You loved him?'

She swallowed on the sudden hard lump in her throat. 'I wasn't sure whether I did or not. It was one of the reasons I came out here looking for my father. I needed time to think about things.'

'And instead you found yourself with yet another problem. Was it a difficult decision?'

'Staying?' She shook her head, still not looking at him. 'Easier than it should have been. I needed an excuse.'

'But you might still have gone back to him after your father died if circumstances had been different?'

'No.' This time she forced herself to meet the blue eyes. 'There was too much lacking in our relationship. You'd taught me that much.'

Raoul's smile was faint. 'You mean he couldn't arouse you the same way. Perhaps he was simply lacking in technique.'

'Perhaps he was.' She said it stiffly. 'He didn't have your experience.' There was a pause, then she sighed. 'I'm sorry, I shouldn't have said that.'

'Why not, if it's what you feel?' He sounded unmoved. 'I've known other women in the past, yes. Whether I have need of them in the future is largely up to you.'

She drew in a slow breath. 'You're saying I could keep you content?'

'Is that so unlikely?'

'Not now perhaps, but later when I'm ...' She paused, trying to find the right words. 'Did you ever find pregnant women desirable?'

'No,' he admitted. 'But then I was never personally involved before.' He studied her with drawn brows. 'You do want this child?'

'Of course I want it.' The answer was too quick, too emphatic. She made some attempt to mute the image, 'I'd have preferred it to happen some other way, that's all.'

Humour touched his lips. 'How many ways are there?'

'You know what I mean.'

'Yes,' he agreed, 'I know what you mean.' He waited a bare moment before reaching out an unexpected hand to take her coffee cup from her and place it on the table before them alongside his own. His expression was serious again. 'Vanessa, I have to be honest with you. There was never a time when I actually contemplated marriage where you were concerned, but that isn't to say I might not have if Crystal hadn't already consented to marry me. I was wrong to start the affair with you at all under the circumstances, only matters got out of hand. There were times during those weeks after you left Royale when I wanted to see you, especially when your father died. In the end I compromised by asking Pierre to attend the funeral and report back to me on how you were. When he told me about the baby I could hardly bring myself to believe I was the father. Once I was convinced there was only one course I could take—one course I wanted to take.' He paused, watching her reaction, face softening at the look in her eyes. His hand lifted again, this time to smooth the line of her cheek. 'We still have what we started with. Will it be so difficult to extend the emotion in time?'

She didn't need time; it was right there in her heart this very moment. Only the words wouldn't come. Not yet. Not until he could say them too, and mean it.

'No,' she said instead. 'I don't think it will.' Her smile was just a little tremulous. 'You're a very special man, Raoul.'

'So?' Blue eyes sparked a sudden invitation. 'Come and show me how special.'

She laughed with him, allowing herself to be drawn into his arms. His kiss was lacking in passion yet all the more comforting for it. She clung to him, putting her head down to his chest with a feeling of coming home. No more regrets. From now on she only looked ahead. This was Raoul's child she was carrying and she wanted it very much. For the first time she actually wanted it.

Choosing a car for her own use proved more of a problem than Vanessa had anticipated. By choice she was drawn to the sports' models, yet was bound to concede that getting in and out of low-slung doors might prove something of a difficulty in the weeks to come. In the end she settled for a more sedate but scarcely less expensive Vanden Plas saloon with every imaginable refinement and an automatic drive, insisting on driving it home there and then with Raoul following.

'It's a dream of a car,' she confided over lunch, unable to contain her pleasure in possession. 'I only ever had a Mini before, and that wasn't exactly new.'

'No lingering regrets over the Porsche?' asked Raoul, smiling at her enthusiasm, and she wrinkled her nose.

'Well, maybe just a couple, but it was hardly practical. I never drive faster than sixty anyway, so it would have been wasted on me.'

'A little,' he agreed. 'What are you going to do with yourself this afternoon? I have to go back to town myself.'

'I thought I might drive over to see Simone,' she said.

'A good idea. I'm glad the two of you have become such good friends.'

He wasn't alone in that, Vanessa reflected. Simone and Pierre Renaud were the only real friends she could count on so far. She dreaded the Friday evening still, although determined to put on a show for Raoul's sake. These people would be only too ready to compare her with Crystal, and were as unlikely to be impressed by any lack of confidence on her part as Raoul himself had been the other day. He needed a wife capable of handling all occasions, so that was what she would endeavour to be.

Looking at him now she felt the soft warmth stealing through her. Difficult to believe that so devastating a man really belonged to her. Last night there had been tenderness in his lovemaking, not just fleetingly but all the way through. They had entered a new phase of their relationship, and no going back.

His slow smile and faint lift of a brow brought a flush to her cheek as she realised he knew exactly what she was thinking about. Well, not exactly perhaps. His memories would no doubt be more physically than emotionally orientated.

'I thought we might have dinner out tonight,' he said. 'A kind of belated celebration. We've been married ten whole days.'

How would it feel ten years from now? Vanessa wondered, making the appropriate response. It was a question only time could answer.

Simone was delighted as always to see her. She was preparing a meal for the evening in the large country-style kitchen.

'It's Mira's day off,' she explained, 'and Pierre has an engagement this evening so we must eat earlier than usual. Do you like cooking, Vanessa?'

'Yes,' she acknowledged. 'Only I doubt if Kalani is going to let me into her kitchen. She never takes a real day off. Bel Air is her whole life.'

'You should insist. You're the mistress of the house not Kalani.'

Vanessa laughed. 'Try telling her that! Anyway, I'd hate to get across her before Friday. She might decide to leave me with dinner for ten.'

'You'd cope,' the other returned with comforting assurance. Her dark eyes twinkled. 'Today I have the feeling you could cope with anything. Is a new car all it takes to make you so happy—or might Raoul himself have something to do with the change in you?'

'We had a long talk last night,' Vanessa confided. She hesitated a moment before adding slowly, 'Simone, how did you feel when you first knew Christian was on the way?'

'Sick,' came the prompt reply. 'For the first weeks I could think of little else but that. For me the joy began the first time I felt him kick. Until then there had been no seperate identity in my mind.' She laughed. 'Pierre would spend many entranced moments watching the movement under my skin. Men are so proud of their achievement.'

Vanessa could believe that. Raoul would make a good father—a caring father. They would be a family.

Simone came out to admire the car before she left. 'A sensible choice,' she conceded. 'Crystal was a menace on the roads with that Porsche of hers. I suppose she had it shipped out when she left.'

'I imagine she did.' Vanessa was telling herself not to be a fool. Raoul hadn't been comparing the two of them. Yet try as she might she couldn't rid herself of the image in her mind's eye: the two of them side by side in the close confines of those bucket seats; Crystal's hands so confident on the wheel, her tawny eyes laughing, challenging him. He drove fast himself; he would admire a woman with the same ability to handle a car. What must his feelings have been this morning following her from town at such a sedate pace? Life had to be duller for him, no matter how willing his spirit.

She refused to allow depression to overtake her during the drive home. Crystal was gone. He would forget her in time. Everything boiled down to time in the end. If only she could persuade herself there was going to be enough of it.

Raoul flew up to the mine on the Tuesday. Vanessa would have liked to accompany him on the trip, but didn't like to ask. He would be staying overnight and returning the following afternoon, he told her. On no account would he be late for the dinner party.

Vanessa reached the *Julia* shortly after nine-thirty on the Friday morning to find Brenden ready and waiting to cast off.

'I hoped you'd come,' he said, 'but I wasn't sure. Did Raoul object?'

'He doesn't know,' she admitted. 'I'm only here at all because I want to settle something with you.'

'If it's about the boat the answer's the same,' he responded stubbornly. 'She's half yours, Van. There's no getting away from it.'

'Except that I don't want it, and Raoul doesn't want me to have it. He suggested I present you with a *fait accompli*.'

'He wants to cut you off from association with me, is that it?' The thin face had a wry expression. 'Understandable, I suppose.' He paused a moment or two, then shrugged. 'If it's making life difficult for you, what can I say? I don't merit any of it, but I'm not going to kick providence in the teeth by turning it down.'

They were making out into the lagoon, creating a welcome breeze in their passage. Vanessa turned her face into the wind, remembering the early days when the three of them had been together. It was little more than two weeks since her father's death, she realised in shock. It seemed so much longer. They had never become close the way father and daughter should be, but she liked to think her presence had made a difference to him those final days.

'Do you think you'll stay her in Caledonia once you're a free agent?' she asked casually, watching the way he handled the wheel. 'The *Julia* is ocean-going, isn't she?'

'Big enough to handle the islands,' he agreed. 'I don't know. I'll need time to think about it.' His smile came and went. 'There'd be a few who'd be highly relieved if the competition was reduced. I always wanted to see Fiji and Tonga, I admit. Maybe I should take the opportunity.'

They changed the subject after that, each aware that
the die had been cast. The day was hot, and growing
hotter, though it was pleasant on the water. Vanessa
rolled up the legs of her cotton jeans in order to get
the sun to them until Brenden fished out a bikini she
had left on board.

'I meant to send it to you,' he said. 'Only it seemed
a bit ridiculous considering how old it was. Why don't
you put it on? It would be a whole lot more
comfortable than those pants of yours.'

A whole lot easier on the waistline, anyway, she
thought, tempted. Why not? Apart from that slight
thickening and a certain rounding out, there was little
enough to see as yet. She might even take a swim. It
was supposed to be good excercise in pregnancy.

She changed in the cabin, a little self-conscious
initially when she emerged but not for long. Brenden
had anchored off a sand bar some quarter of a mile
from the shoreline. The bathing here was safe, she
knew, because they had used it in the past.
Accustomed to diving in from the side of the boat, she
thought nothing of it now, cleaving the water cleanly
to surface several yards away. The temperature felt
colder than she had anticipated, or perhaps she was
simply too hot. She did a vigorous few yards crawl in
order to speed up her circulation.

'Come on in,' she called to Brenden, circling back to
the boat. 'It feels great!'

He shook his head. 'I'll stay here and watch.' There
was a slight hesitation before he tagged on diffidently,
'Are you sure you should be doing this?'

Vanessa laughed, shaking water from her hair. 'I'm
fine. It's been weeks since I was in the sea! It will
probably be weeks again, so I'm going to make the
most of it.'

She stayed in for about twenty minutes, dragged out eventually only because she didn't want to overdo it. 'I'm out of condition,' she claimed as Brenden helped her back on board. 'Time was when I could have swum to shore and back without a single muscle aching!'

'It doesn't take long,' he agreed. He had fetched a towel up from below. Handing it over, he added, 'I'll go and make some coffee.'

Vanessa dried herself quickly, then stretched out in the warmth of the sun to recover her breath. The dull ache in her back and lower limbs was spreading to all parts of her body. Just a little muscle strain, she told herself reassuringly. Nothing to worry about.

Brenden came back with the coffee to find her sitting up with arms clasped about bent knees and a fixed smile on her lips.

'Sorry it took so long,' he said. 'I had to change cylinders.' He handed over a mug and sat down with his own, taking a gulp of the aromatic brew. 'That's good, even if I do say it myself!'

Raising her own mug to her lips, Vanessa started to drink, only to break off with a sudden exclamation as pain gripped her. It didn't last long before subsiding again to the same dull ache, but she knew it would be back.

'What is it?' Brenden was on his feet, face anxious as he took in her pallor. 'Van . . .'

She tried to say it calmly. 'I think you'd better get me back to Noumea.'

'The baby?'

'It has to be.' Her eyes were dark pools, already mirroring an inner tragedy. 'Make it quick, Bren . . . please!'

Going all out it took them twenty-five minutes. Brenden had had the presence of mind to radio through ahead for an ambulance to be waiting when they berthed. What followed was a blur of wailing sirens, of white corridors, of hovering faces and racking pain, the whole overlaid by the knowledge that she herself had caused this thing to happen and the dreadful creeping sense of loss.

She awoke to an unfamiliar bed and a total blankness of mind, lying for several seconds just staring at the plain white ceiling. Memory returned bit by bit, filling in the detail until the whole sorry picture was complete. Not a bad dream but reality, and too late for regrets. Not too late for sorrow though. It lay like a weight on her chest.

There was movement at the side of the bed, the sound of a chair being pushed back. Vanessa turned her head slowly to meet Raoul's eyes, holding the blue gaze for bare moments before lowering her own.

'I'm sorry,' she murmured painfully. 'I've let you down.'

'You mustn't think about it,' he said. 'It's over and done.'

'I can't simply forget it,' she refuted. 'Anymore than you can. The only reason you married me was because of the baby.'

He could hardly dispute that fact; to do him credit he didn't attempt to do so. 'So we try again,' he said. 'You're young and healthy. You'll get over this quite quickly, I'm told.'

Physically perhaps, she thought, but what about mentally? There had been a time when she hadn't wanted this baby, it was true, but not this past week. He had become a part of her: attained an identity. And she had killed him. Not deliberately, oh no, but her carelessness had been equally criminal. She couldn't begin to think about creating a replacement. Not yet, at any rate. Raoul was being cold and callous in even suggesting it. But then it wasn't her he was thinking about, was it? He had offered no shred of sympathy for what she had gone through.

'How long will I be in this place?' she asked.

'Overnight. I'm to fetch you home in the morning after your own gynaecologist has seen you.'

His home, not hers, she thought. Not anymore. She had never belonged there. She closed her eyes before the tears could properly form, clenching her teeth against the sudden need to reach out and feel his hand take hers. 'I'm tired,' she said. 'Do you mind if we talk later. I'd like to sleep now.'

It was a moment or two before he moved. When he did it was abruptly, without a single word of farewell. Vanessa turned over and buried her face in the pillows. She had never felt so totally alone in her life.

The gynaecologist arrived at nine the next morning to find her both outwardly and inwardly in suitable shape to leave the hospital.

She was young and in excellent health, he advised, unconsciously repeating the words Raoul himself had used the previous night. There was no reason at all why she shouldn't conceive again at once if that was her wish. Many found solace in doing just that. Vanessa reserved comment either way, leaving him to the obvious conclusion that she wasn't yet ready to discuss the subject with any objectivity. He told her to come and see him again in a month and left it at that.

Raoul arrived at ten with her things. Dressed in crisp cool white cotton, Vanessa surveyed herself with lack-lustre eyes through the wall mirror and wondered what kind of a night he had spent. At a time like this most husbands and wives would be drawn together in their mutual grief. If Raoul would only walk back in here now and take her in his arms it would make all the difference in the world. She knew it was unlikely. Whatever emotional attachment he had felt had been towards the mother of his child. She was his wife still, but the title had a hollow ring.

There was little in his manner to refute her fears when he did come to get her. He was courteous, solicitous of her comfort, and as impersonal as a stranger. Seated at his side in the car as they headed away from the hospital, Vanessa let the words come of their own accord, unsurprised by the flat intonation.

'So what do we do now?'

He took his time in answering, concentrating on the morning traffic. 'About what?' he asked at length.

Her laugh was short, sharp and lacking in humour of any kind. 'It's called lost freedom. We can hardly ask for an annulment so it has to be divorce. How difficult will that be here?'

'The question doesn't arise,' he said harshly. 'We made a contract and we're staying with it. There can be other babies.'

'I don't want another.' She almost choked on the hard lump in her throat. 'Once was more than enough.'

'You'll get over it.' His tone was designed to hurt. 'Next time I'll make sure you carry it full term.'

She had suspected all along what he was thinking, but it was something else again to have it put into words. She said thickly, 'You really believe I made this happen?'

'What am I supposed to believe? You had little enough enthusiasm for having the child.'

'That's not true!'

'No?' He glanced at her briefly, face unrelenting. 'It's the impression you gave.'

'Only because I felt so trapped.'

'We were both trapped,' he pointed out. 'If I could adjust then you should have been able to do the same. I began to have hopes that everything was going to work out between us the other night. It still can.'

'Providing I give you another child?'

'Eventually, yes.'

'Supposing I couldn't conceive again?'

'Unlikely, considering how easily you did it the first time.' There was a pause, then he sighed, shaking his head. 'This isn't the time to be discussing it. Give it a week or two and we'll both be better equipped. Simone asked me to tell you she'll be over this afternoon, if you want to see her. You could 'phone her from home.'

Vanessa made the anticipated response, leaning back wearily in her seat. Raoul was right. There was little point in discussing it now. Later, when he had had time to think about it he would realise that divorce was the only real solution. They should never have married in the first place. Too much had been against them. If she had gone away as she had planned the baby might still be alive inside her this moment.

Kalani provided all the sympathy anyone could need. Vanessa responded because she did so desperately need it. She felt nothing when Raoul announced he had to get back to town. There was no cause for him to stay.

She telephoned Simone with the intention of putting her off, changing her mind at the last moment because the idea of being alone held even less appeal. The Frenchwoman arrived around two, blessedly warm and uncritical.

'We all of us do things without thinking,' she said, recognising the guilt in Vanessa's rendering of the story. 'Nine times out of ten we're fortunate enough to do no lasting damage. You must have twisted something inside when you dived. Next time you . . .'

'Everyone talks about next time as if it were the only panacea needed,' Vanessa broke in roughly. 'Like replacing a kitten or a puppy!'

Simone smiled, refusing to take offence. 'It has its similarities when it comes to the matter of compensation. I also miscarried the first time I was pregnant, so I do know what I'm talking about.'

'You did?' Vanessa's expression was suddenly wry. 'And here I am acting as I were the only one it ever happened to! What was the cause?'

'No apparent reason. In some ways that was worse because it could always happen again. Christian was doubly precious to me as the proof that I could carry full term after all, although I did take special care, I admit.'

Vanessa looked out over the grounds to the sea, eyes blind. 'It was different for you. You had a normal marriage contracted out of love not duty. Raoul wants a son and heir, nothing else.'

'I think you're wrong. Raoul needs love, the way any man does, and not just physically. You were both of you on the verge of it the last time I saw you together. You can be again if you allow it to happen. Not that it's the most important element in a good marriage by any means. I would say mutual respect and liking were more essential as a basis.'

Out on all three counts, thought Vanessa dully. Whatever chance there might have been for them once she had killed it as surely and carelessly as she had killed their child.

CHAPTER NINE

'I have to go to Tokyo for a few days,' Raoul announced without preamble over the dinner table, arousing Vanessa from her listless contemplation of the plate just set before her. 'I'd ask you to come with me if I thought for a moment you'd be interested.'

She lifted her shoulders, not even bothering to pretend. 'What would I do there?'

'The same thing you do here, I imagine. That's exactly the point.' His tone was harsher. 'It's been two weeks. We have to start picking up the threads again sometime. Perhaps a few days on your own might help you come to terms with things.'

Vanessa doubted it. A problem such as theirs was not to be resolved by thought alone. To all intents and purposes she had spent the past two weeks isolated from this man she had married. They shared the same table, even the same bed, but there the communication stopped. A trip to Tokyo wasn't going to change anything.

'When do you leave?' she asked.

'Tomorrow morning. Early. I'll be gone before you're awake.'

She doubted that too. His least movement had her awake, tensed for the approach that never came. When the time did come she wasn't sure how she was going to react. The very notion of physical union left her cold. Last time she had been gone on his return; might not the same solution serve again? Perhaps he would be secretly relieved to have the decision taken out of his hands that way.

'I hope you have a good journey,' she said politely, as to a stranger. 'And a productive one.'

His mouth tilted sardonically. 'You're so sure it's business?'

'What else?' Her tone hadn't altered. 'Unless you have a Geisha or two stashed away.'

'Geishas don't provide the kind of service you have in mind,' came the hard retort. 'Although I daresay if I had need of a woman that way one might be found.'

'On the premise that money buys everything?' she flashed, momentarily jerked from her indifference, and saw him smile again.

'At least something can reach you. Don't read meanings that aren't there. If money was all it took there would be no problem.'

She relaxed again forcibly. 'So I was being over-sensitive. You can hardly blame me. There was a time when you were convinced that was all I was after.'

'I have to be allowed my quota of mistakes,' he returned on a milder note. 'I know you'd walk out on me tomorrow if I gave you the chance, which is why I have your passport safely under lock and key. You can have it back the day you present me with a son.'

'I'd hardly be leaving alone.'

'It would be the only way. Naturally I'd prefer you to stay. A child needs a mother.'

'More than you need a wife.'

The dark head inclined. 'Again that's largely up to you. We may never regain the ground we lost, but we could manage a reasonable marriage. We'll never know unless we try.'

She took a moment or two before making any reply, eyes searching his face. A breeze had sprung up, stirring the honeysuckle growing over the balustrade to release its scent. She was reminded suddenly of the evenings they had spent together on Royale, so many weeks ago now. If she had known then what was to happen would she have been capable of turning away? Easy to say yes; in retrospect everything was easy.

'I don't think I could bear to have you touch me again,' she said with calculated malice. 'That's going to make things difficult, isn't it?' She pushed back her chair abruptly. 'It's turned cool. I'll take my coffee indoors.'

Raoul stayed where he was, at least she assumed he did. He still hadn't put in an appearance at ten when she decided to go to bed. As on other nights, she hurried through her toilette in order to be between sheets and ostensibly asleep when he came in. She doubted if the act deceived him, but it made things easier.

It was almost midnight before he did arrive. Lying there with face turned to the window, she listened to the familiar sounds as he prepared for bed, visualising the lean, lithe body as he stepped under the shower and turned the jet to full. They had showered together more than once, dissolving laughter into passion as they rinsed away the soap. The memory could stir her still. If she got up now and went to him he would take her in, but it wouldn't be the same.

Silence as the water was turned off, then after a moment or two the sound of a door opening; footsteps coming across the floor. Vanessa remained motionless when the sheet was lifted, feeling the mattress move slightly to his added weight. The arm encircling her from behind was firm and unyielding, hauling her against him. He was naked, she realised in that frozen moment of inaction, and already aroused.

'Don't!' she jerked out, holding herself rigid. 'It isn't going to be any use, Raoul!'

He rolled her to face him, using his weight to keep her there. His eyes were dark with determination, his mouth merciless. 'You're wrong,' he said. 'It's the only way we're going to break down the barriers.'

He didn't so much break them down as dismantle them, taking his time as her body came slowly and reluctantly alive under his skilful manipulation. Resistance ebbed, giving way to desire. Her lips parted hungrily beneath his, tongue touching, arms twining, reaching out. Why didn't matter. Not here and now. That would come later when she had time to think clearly again.

He kissed her breasts, fingers encircling the aching fullness, lingering almost too long before gliding on and down over the flat plane of her stomach to caress the soft skin of her thighs with a motion both stimulating and relaxing at one and the same time. Rolling, she pressed her lips to his chest with a little moan, trailing her hand across the hard arch of his hipbone to the tune of his roughened breath. So familiar the feel of him, so wonderfully, intoxicatingly good. How could she ever have imagined that she could live without this man? He meant everything to her. He always had. She said his name as he came into her, enfolding him with supple limbs. Then they were moving together in the matchless rhythm, soaring into that wide blue yonder where time itself ceased to exist.

It was eight o'clock before she awoke. Raoul would already be on his way to the airport, she realised, subsiding back into the pillows. She wished now that she had gone with him. Lying here alone, all the old doubts and fears came back to plague her. No matter how wonderful last night had been the motive behind

Raoul's approach was only too plain. She was the instrument, that was all. What she had failed to give him the first time round she could always supply again.

So why not let it happen? came the thought. Marriages had been cemented together by the advent of a child before this. No matter how Raoul felt about her, there was no getting away from the fact that she loved him desperately. Everything else had been a pretence, a self-protection. Half a loaf had to be better than none.

She swam for the first time since the miscarriage that morning, and felt as though she had crossed a bridge. From now on there was to be no looking back. Kalani was happy to see the change in her, and said so, causing Vanessa to wonder just how much of the situation the Polynesian woman had guessed. She was on the terrace when the call came through for her. One of the staff brought the handset out to her, plugging it in to the extension under the table. Brenden sounded odd, almost diffident, as he asked after her health.

'Any chance of you coming down to the boat?' he tagged on. 'I've got something for you.'

Vanessa hesitated. 'What kind of something?'

'It's a surprise. I could make us lunch.' He paused before adding tentatively, 'You're not blaming me for what happened, are you, Van?'

'Of course not.' She was quick to deny the implication. 'It was my own stupid fault for diving overboard.'

'Then you'll come?'

To refuse now would be hurtful, she thought. Ownership of the *Julia* had already been transferred into Brenden's name. No doubt he simply wanted to show his appreciation of the gesture, and perhaps to tell her what his plans were. If he did leave Caledonia she would most probably never see him again.

'I'll be there in about half an hour,' she said.

The streets were settling into their midday tranquillity when she drove through the town. From now until two o'clock everything stopped for lunch. She reached the wharf on the hour, leaving the car parked under the shade of an awning. This might be the last time she would walk these boards, she reflected with a tinge of nostalgia as she made her way out to where the *Julia* was berthed. So much had happened in the past three months; she hoped the next three proved happier.

Brenden was waiting for her on deck, wearing the almost inevitable shorts and T-shirt. He gave her a hand to come aboard, viewing her with a critical eye as she smoothed a hand over her tailored white slacks.

'You look good,' he observed. 'Better than I expected. Are you really recovered?'

'It doesn't take long,' she said lightly. 'Not at ten weeks. I can't stay too long, Bren. I promised to call in on Simone Renaud on the way home.'

'It won't take long.' He stood back to allow her prior access to the hatch. 'Come on below.'

The companionway was short and steep, the treads narrow. Vanessa went down it watching where she put her feet, only becoming aware of the man already occupying the cabin as he rose to his feet from the leeward berth. For a brief, arrested moment she could only stare, taking in the thick fair hair, the square-cut features, the questioning brown eyes. Her mind felt totally blank.

'Hallo, Vanessa,' he said. 'You haven't altered.'

Not altered? She wanted suddenly to laugh. If only he knew just how different a person she was from the girl he had seen off at Heathrow!

'Why now?' she asked, trying to get a grip on herself. 'It's been more than three months, Michael.'

'It's taken me that long to get the time off,' he said. 'Even then I had to plead extenuating circumstances.' He hesitated, the hurt quite plain in his eyes. 'You could have let me know the way things were. So far as I knew the only thing keeping you here was your father. Now I find him dead and you married. It's been pretty much shock on shock.'

'It must have been.' She hardly knew what to say to him. 'I don't have any excuses. When you didn't answer my letter I just assumed you'd accepted it.'

'I didn't answer it because I knew you well enough to realise I wasn't going to change your mind that way. I wanted to assess the situation for myself—try and find a way round the problem.' His smile was wry. 'I even considered taking your father back to England with us if that would help resolve matters.'

'Oh, God, I'm sorry.' It hurt to talk. 'I really am sorry!'

The shrug did nothing to disguise his feelings. 'What's done is done. You can at least sit down and talk to me, seeing I am here.'

She did so nervelessly, conscious for the first time that Brenden had not followed her down to the saloon. There was nothing she could either say or do that would lessen the blow, but if nothing else she owed him an explanation.

'I suppose Brenden already filled you in on the main detail,' she said. 'I don't expect you to understand. It just . . . happened, that's all.'

'You mean this man set out to seduce you?'

'No. At least . . .' She paused, biting her lip. 'It wasn't like that. Not wholly. I didn't exactly discourage him.'

Brown eyes winced. 'Considering how long it took me to get you into bed, he must have had quite a way with him. Was it better than with me?'

Numbly she shook her head, despising herself for the lie yet not prepared to undermine his masculine pride any further. 'Just different. You've a right to be bitter. I can't complain no matter what you call me.'

'I'm not calling you anything,' he denied. 'At his age he has to have a whole lot more experience than you. Why the devil couldn't he take some precautions?'

'For the same reason you didn't,' Vanessa returned without malice. 'Because he assumed it was already taken care of.'

Michael shook his head. 'I assumed nothing. We agreed you . . .'

'All right, we agreed.' She spread her hands in a weary little gesture. 'It doesn't matter how it happened, just that it did. What else would you have had me do other than marry him, given the chance?'

He said softly, 'You could have come home to me.'

She stared at him. 'Carrying another man's child?'

'If you'd told me it was mine I wouldn't have known the difference.' He forestalled her reply with another lift of his shoulders. 'Anyway, it's immaterial now, isn't it? Our friend out there tells me you lost it.'

'True.' She was fighting to stay on top of the situation. 'I'm still married to Raoul.'

'You don't have to stay married.'

'Even if I want to be?'

He studied her for a long moment, his mouth slowly twisting. 'Of course. Why should you give up all that!'

'It doesn't have anything to do with money,' she denied. 'Raoul wants a son.'

'And you feel you owe him?' Michael leaned forward suddenly, taking hold of her hands. 'Vanessa, you can't be serious about this! It's your whole life you're talking about. The man doesn't have any feeling for you.'

She said painfully, 'How can you be so sure?'

'Because he didn't even bother to come near you during those weeks you were waiting for your father to die. He'd had you and that would have been that if you hadn't presented him with a problem. I can admire a man who stands by his responsibilities, but not one who tries to use guilt as a lever to get his own way. If he wants a son that badly there must be a dozen women who'd be glad to oblige.'

'But none already bearing his name.' She drew in a slow breath. 'I'm not sure exactly how much Brenden's told you and how much you're simply surmising, but there's no question of my getting a divorce. If you'll let me, I'd like to reimburse you for what it must have cost you to come out here, because it's entirely my fault that you are here.'

'I don't care about the money,' he said, refusing to let go of her hands. 'I just care about you, Vanessa. If you'd married another man because you loved him it would be different, but I'm not going to stand by and see you used this way.'

'You'll have to.' She was pale, but in command of herself. 'I never wanted to hurt you, Michael. I think too much of you for that. Only it's too late. You have to see that.'

'It's never too late.' There was determination in the set of his jaw. 'I have another three weeks before I have to get back. Brenden already offered me a berth here on the boat if I want it. Just promise me that if anything happens to change your mind you'll come and tell me, will you? No strings. I just want you to know I'm here, that's all.'

The offer stirred her, the way it was meant to. She looked at him with tears prickling the backs of her eyes. Raoul would never love her the way this man loved her. Michael had come half way round the world just to find her. How could she disregard his appeal?

'I promise,' she said.

Brenden was sitting aft in one of the swivel chairs when she finally went back on deck. He spun to look at her, expression defensive.

'I had to do it that way to get you down here,' he said. 'He was threatening to come up to the house.'

'You did right,' Vanessa told him. 'I had to see him.'

'What did you tell Raoul?'

'He left for Tokyo this morning.'

'But you are going to tell him?'

'I don't know.' She made a helpless little gesture. 'What's the point?'

'The point is you've got a man in there who'd follow you to the ends of the earth if necessary. I'd have thought that was worth a whole lot.'

'It is,' she agreed. Her voice was low, her smile rueful. 'More than I deserve. The problem is, he isn't the right man.'

Brenden was silent for a moment, thin features unusually serious. 'If it has to come down to a straight choice,' he said at length, 'I think I'd settle for being the one loved rather than the one loving. It's a lot less painful.'

He was right about that at least, Vanessa conceded drily. Not that it made any difference to her situation. There was always hope to sustain her.

'I shan't be coming back,' she said. 'I feel awful about it, but it's for the best. I already told Michael how I felt.'

'And he accepted it?'

'Not yet.' She waited a moment before adding slowly, 'If you withdrew your offer to put him up here on the *Julia* he might decide to go on back home.'

'I doubt it. Not from what he said earlier. If I withdraw the offer he'll simply move into a hotel for the next few weeks. You wouldn't want him to spend any more money, would you?'

She shook her head, sighing. 'No more than he has to. I doubt if he can really afford it.'

'Well then, you'll have to leave things the way they are. He's done some sailing, it turns out, so he can crew for me to earn his keep. Salvage his pride a little.'

'You were going to Fiji.'

'I can do that anytime. That's where I'm lucky. I don't have any ties.'

Lucky indeed, she thought. Right now she would have given a great deal to be as free. The wave of homesickness almost finished her. There was so much she missed—even the soft English drizzle. Seeing Michael again had brought it all back, just when she had believed herself over the worst. Living in luxury meant nothing. She could give it all up tomorrow without a pang. The only thing keeping her here at present was Raoul himself. Was she a fool to sacrifice so much for so little return?

The following few days crawled by. There was no word from Raoul, but then she hadn't expected any. So far as he was concerned they had settled their future. Already she could be pregnant again. There was no medical reason why not. Wakening on the morning of his return to evidence that she wasn't brought mixed reactions. Raoul obviously still got something out of making love to her, so it was going to be no particular penance for him to repeat the performance. The problem lay with her; in her knowledge that she was just a means to an end. Once he had what he wanted from her he might very well lose interest altogether.

She thought of Michael, stirred once more by his tenacity. He might never have provided the kind of fulfilment she had found in Raoul's arms, but she was only just beginning to learn how much more to life there was than that fleeting satisfaction. Michael was safe, he was reliable, yet not lacking in spirit either when he could do as he had done. He had so much to offer. More than she had ever realised. And it wasn't too late. Raoul couldn't keep her here if she really made up her mind to go.

It was evening before he arrived home. He seemed different, Vanessa thought, watching him surreptitiously over dinner; certainly he was preoccupied. Despite their differences, they had never been short of conversation. Tonight he showed a marked lack of enthusiasm for idle chat.

'You must be tired,' she said during one of the long pauses. 'Crossing the equator twice inside a week has to have an effect—to say nothing of what you've been doing in between.'

Something flickered for a brief moment in the blue eyes. 'I wasn't so tied up that I didn't have time to think,' he said. He paused again as if to choose his words. When he did speak it was with obvious difficulty. 'Vanessa, I've been wrong in trying to force you to give me another child. We need time to find ourselves first. I realise it may already be too late, but I . . .'

'It isn't.' A cautious warmth was beginning to steal through her. 'I'm not pregnant again. Not this time.'

His smile had a wry edge. 'Perhaps I'm not so virile after all. Anyway, it certainly makes things easier.' His eyes sought hers again, the expression in them still difficult to define with any accuracy. 'How would you like to go out to Royale for a week or so—just the two of us? It would give us the breathing space we need.'

Royale. Where it had all begun. Her own eyes were luminous, belying the restraint in her voice. 'I'd like it very much. When can we go?'

'A few days, no more. Once we're there we'll disconnect the 'phone and be alone.'

'Hardly alone with a staff like Royale's.' She searched his face, hardly yet believing he meant what he appeared to be saying. 'Why now, Raoul? What happened to make you like this?'

'I finally realised where my priorities lay,' he said softly. 'We're going to start again, Vanessa. Right from the beginning. Only this time there'll be no mistakes.'

He wasn't saying he loved her. Not yet. But he would when the time was right. She could wait until then.

Simone rang through after breakfast to check that Raoul was home and invite the two of them over for dinner that same evening.

'Just the four of us,' she said. 'So no formality. Pierre likes his weekends free of ties in every sense.' She laughed at her own little joke. 'Tell Raoul I look forward to seeing the kimono he promised to bring me the next time he visited Tokyo.'

'I forgot,' Raoul confessed when Vanessa passed on the message. He added lightly, 'I even forgot to bring my own wife a present!'

Vanessa laughed. 'I'm glad you didn't. I might have taken it as a sign of a guilty conscience.'

His smile seemed to stiffen. 'About what?'

'Well, you did threaten to visit a Geisha.' She eyed him curiously. 'Did you? Ever, I mean.'

'A couple of times,' he acknowledged. 'It isn't as exciting as you seem to imagine. For one thing it's always a group meeting—a business mens' luncheon or something similar. The Geishas are trained to entertain with singing and dancing or conversation. Perhaps certain ones might be persuaded into a more intimate relationship if the incentive was right, but it's frowned on.' He was relaxed now, deliberately taunting as he tagged on, 'The bathhouse now, that's another thing altogether. A man could get to like it with little trouble at all.'

They continued through the day in that vein: friendly, chaffing, not lover-like but somehow closer than they had even been. It was well into the dry season now, with the temperatures slightly lower on average than earlier in the year and the evenings relatively cool. For the Renauds Vanessa chose to wear a pants suit in a lilac-coloured silk jersey that brought out the highlights in her hair. The latter was quite long now, its natural curl tamed into shining obedience by regular visits to Noumea's top stylist. Comparing her reflection in the dressing-mirror with the remembered image of three months ago, Vanessa could only acknowledge the difference money made. She might never be beautiful but she could hold her own. She could even contemplate her eventual emergence into the island's social scene with equanimity.

Raoul himself was wearing tailored cream slacks and a black shirt open at the throat on the familiar glint of gold. From the top of his dark head to the tips of his Gucci shoes he was every inch the Frenchman, lean, arrogant and possessed of that inherent sensuality that even now could make her pulses race. He had barely touched her since his return, although his manner was far from aloof. He had to know how she felt about him; he couldn't fail to know. Why was he holding back?

'If you're ready,' he said, not glancing her way as he bent to pick up his jacket from the bed, 'we should go. It's almost eight now.'

Simone looked radiant that evening. Raoul told her so the moment he saw her. It wasn't until she and Vanessa were temporarily alone together later in the evening that she let her secret drop, and even then with reluctance.

'I had it confirmed the very day you had the accident,' she said wryly. 'I wouldn't be telling you now except that you're going to have to know sometime.'

'I'm happy for you,' Vanessa assured her, and really meant it. Her smile was warm, and not in the least bit wobbly. 'I'm glad you did tell me. When is it due?'

'March.' Simone laughed. 'If it turns out to be twins again I think Pierre will decide enough is enough. For myself, I hope it is. Perhaps boys this time so that Christian won't be too lonely, although he will have to wait a while.' She slanted a glance. 'Perhaps we may share the experience even yet.'

'Perhaps.' If Raoul had meant what he had said last night it was doubtful, but not beyond the realms of possibility. 'Is Pierre to tell Raoul?'

'No, I thought it kinder if you did that.'

Vanessa waited until they were halfway home before doing so, watching the faint twist of his lips.

'Simone is becoming over-sensitive,' he remarked. 'Last time I was the first to know. I'm godfather to Christian.'

'She wants me to be godmother to the new baby,' Vanessa admitted. 'I suppose it's a bit early, but I naturally said yes. She's over the moon about it.' She glanced at his profile, etched against the window, said hesitantly, 'Raoul, you still don't believe I meant to miscarry, do you?'

'No.' His tone was rueful. 'Even if you didn't particularly want the child I doubt if you're capable of that kind of calculation. I was distraught at the time myself. Not that I'm trying to find excuses. I had no right to say what I did.'

'I did want it,' she said. 'Not initially, perhaps, but things had changed. Next time I'll take greater care.'

'Next time, we'll both take greater care.' He was smiling, his glance reassuring. 'We'll get there, *chére*.'

It was the first time he had used the endearment outside of lovemaking. He had done it consciously, with purpose; a spoken caress. Vanessa answered in French.

'I think it's time I started really trying with your language, don't you?'

'If it's what you want.' One hand came out lightly to touch her cheek. 'Whatever you want.'

They reached the house before midnight. Raoul left the car out front, taking her hand as they went indoors.

'I feel like a nightcap,' he said. 'Are you going to join me?'

Tonight Vanessa would have joined him in anything, she felt so happy. 'Why not,' she agreed.

There were lights still on in the salon, but Raoul made for the library instead. Seated in one of the deep chairs, Vanessa watched him take glasses from the concealed bar and pour the drinks, loving the lean certainty of his hands; remembering the feel of them on her body. Their lovemaking would be all the better for the enforced wait, frustrating though it seemed at the present. By the time they got to Royale everything would be perfect. They would swim in the sea out at the cove, lie naked in each other's arms on the warm sandy floor of the little hut. Nothing could wipe out the intervening months completely, but they would dim as time went by.

'You'd better make that three,' said Crystal from the doorway, and the dream shattered like fragile glass in a vice. Turning her head, she looked into the tawny eyes, saw the enmity gleam for a brief instant before the glance moved back to Raoul who was standing motionless by the bar, the decanter still uptilted in his hand.

'It isn't going to be that easy,' she said with the same metallic flatness in her voice. 'She's going to hear the truth.

'What truth?' Vanessa barely recognised her own voice. 'What are you talking about?'

'I'd have thought it was obvious.' The other's gaze hadn't moved from Raoul's face. 'We were together in Tokyo not forty-eight hours ago.'

CHAPTER TEN

It was Raoul himself who made the first move, expression unreadable as he completed pouring out the whisky. 'What will you have?' he asked.

'You know my preference.' Crystal was maintaining the same icy calm. 'You should.'

He put ice into another glass, poured gin from the bottle, then filled it with tonic. 'I should have anticipated this,' he said. 'Hell hath no fury . . .'

'You asked for it,' she broke in, composure slipping a little. 'How am I expected to feel?'

'It was a risk you took,' he rejoined on a harder note. 'I was a fool to imagine you'd understood what I tried to tell you.'

'I understood it all right. It simply took me a while to decide what I was going to do about it. You used me, Raoul. You . . .'

'Stop it!' Vanessa's voice was low and ragged, her hands clenched into fists in her lap. 'Spare me the sordid details!' She made herself look at Raoul, hating him the more for not even trying to pretend. 'Just answer me one question. Why bother?'

He knew what she meant, of course. It was there in his eyes. He said levelly, 'I'd prefer to discuss it with you alone. In the meantime, I think you need the brandy.'

'I don't need anything from you,' she said. 'Not now, not ever!' She stood up, limbs nerveless. 'Sort it out between you, I'm going to pack.'

'Not tonight,' Raoul stated. 'Not until we've talked.'

'There's nothing you could say that's going to make any difference,' she responded bitterly. 'I'm not interested in excuses. You two suit each other.'

Crystal moved away from the door as she approached, her expression totally lacking in apology. 'You took what was mine,' she said on a vicious note. 'I simply returned the compliment. Now we're even.'

Vanessa didn't bother to reply. The words would have choked her. A mere ten minutes ago she had walked into this room on cloud nine, now her whole world had fallen apart again. What she was going to do she wasn't sure. All she wanted was to be out of this house, out of Raoul's life. For tonight she'd find a hotel in town. She could ring for a taxi from the bedroom. Just an overnight bag was all she would need. The rest of her own things could be fetched later. She wanted nothing Raoul had bought her— nothing from him at all.

She was already changed into slacks and cotton sweater and was zipping up the small case when he came into the bedroom. He paused in the doorway as she swung it to the floor, viewing her set features with a firming of his own mouth.

'You're going to listen to me,' he stated flatly. 'I'm not letting you walk out this way, Vanessa.'

'You don't have any choice,' she said. 'I have a taxi on its way.'

'It can always wait. The driver won't care providing he gets paid.' He came further into the room and closed the door, standing with his back to it. 'Sit down.'

'I'd rather stand, thanks.' There was no tremor in her voice, just a total lack of expression. 'So what did you want to say?'

He sighed suddenly, spreading his hands. 'I didn't

plan to meet Crystal in Tokyo. I told her I was going, but that was all.'

'You've been in touch with her all the time we've been married?'

'On occasion. I couldn't just cut her out of my life altogether. Not after all those years.'

She said huskily, 'What you really mean is you couldn't put her out of your mind. I'm not blaming you for that, Raoul. I was only a passing fancy until you found out about the baby. Why couldn't you let me go when I wanted you to? Crystal is as capable of producing a son for you as I am.'

'Except that I couldn't see her doing it. I knew her too well.' He hadn't moved from the door; now he leaned against it, as if weary of the whole affair. 'I asked her to marry me in a moment of weakness. I could hardly retract the offer once she'd said yes. I had to hope I was wrong about her. When Pierre told me you were pregnant I had a choice to make. There was no way I could let you take my son.'

'If I'd agreed to an adoption you'd have still married Crystal?'

'At the time, yes. I didn't realise then just how much of her mother there was in her.'

'What difference is all this supposed to make?' Vanessa asked numbly. 'It isn't going to alter the fact that you were with her in Tokyo. What I can't understand is why you altered your tactics where I was concerned.'

The answer came soft. 'Is it beyond the realms of possibility that it could be because I care about you? I've been a fool in more ways than the one. I couldn't see what was right there in front of me.'

Her chin lifted. 'Did the realisation come to you before or after you made love to Crystal?'

'I didn't make love to Crystal,' he said.

'She seems to think you did.'

'No, she wants *you* to believe I did. Retaliation for getting in her way. I should thank her for opening my eyes at last. Her only interest is in what *she* wants. It always was.'

'You mean you were blinded by her beauty all those years?' Vanessa made no attempt to mute the sarcasm. 'I may be all sorts of idiot, Raoul, but I'm not stupid. You thought you could set the two of us up—me to play the dutiful little wife, Crystal the mistress. Like father, like son, isn't that what they say? Only she wouldn't settle for the arrangement. Why should she?'

Raoul was white around the mouth, but he was still in control. 'If that's your considered opinion there doesn't seem to be a lot left to say.'

'There isn't.' She lifted the case, picking up her leather shoulder bag from the bed. 'Are you going to let me pass?'

It was a moment before he moved, opening the door before standing aside. His face was a taut mask. 'I'm not stopping you.'

She passed him without looking at him, heading for the stairs and that long, curving descent into the familiar hall. Crystal stood in the library doorway, glass in hand, a smile on her lips.

'Leaving already?' she mocked. 'What a pity!'

The taxi was coming up the drive as she got outside. The driver gave her a curious look but made no comment when she told him to take her to Le Belvedere. By tomorrow few would be unaware that Raoul DuTemple's wife had spent the night in a hotel. No doubt there would be many who would consider the parting vastly overdue. Tomorrow she had to begin thinking about what she was going to do, for tonight she didn't want to think at all.

She was sitting in the lobby while the maids cleaned her room when Michael turned up around midmorning. A few days in the sun had given him a good colour already, she noted as he came towards her. It suited him.

'Brenden heard the news along the waterfront,' he said without preamble, sitting down beside her. 'What happened, Vanessa?'

'We came to the parting of the ways,' she said unemotionally. 'I'd as soon not talk about it, if you don't mind. Not just yet.'

He was silent for a moment or two, obviously somewhat at a loss. 'So what happens now?' he asked at length. 'Is it irrevocable?'

'Completely.' She could say that with certainty after a night spent reliving that scene in the library. Let Crystal have him if it meant so much to her. She wished them joy of each other. 'I'll probably go back home to England,' she acknowledged. 'I don't have anything to keep me here. He can either divorce me from here on I'll do it myself from there, whichever is quickest.'

'It has to be three years,' Michael said. 'Before you can apply for a divorce, I mean. Unless the law has altered.'

Three years, to dissolve six weeks of married life, Vanessa reflected. Too long by far. 'It will have to be from this end then,' she said. 'Better, anyway. He can claim desertion.' She stirred restlessly. 'I left my passport, and most of my things. Not very good planning, was it?'

'I could collect them for you,' Michael offered. 'Brenden will loan me the car.'

She gazed at him in wonder. 'You'd do that?'

'Someone has to,' he came back practically. 'I wouldn't mind telling him a few home truths of my own!'

'He doesn't know about you,' she said. 'At least, not that you're here in Noumea.'

'Then it's time he found out. Is there likely to be a load of luggage?'

'Not that I'll want. I'll give you a note for Kalani. She's housekeeper. There won't be more than a couple of cases.' Vanessa hesitated, searching the square features. 'You don't have to do this, Michael.'

'I want to,' he said. 'Anyway, who else would you send?'

She had no idea, she was bound to admit, short of going herself. If she could manage to leave Caledonia without seeing Raoul again all the better. Last night she had run the gamut of emotion, this morning she felt blessedly numb. If Michael succeeded in obtaining her passport she could be on a flight out in a couple of days. The bulk of her assets was still in England, thank heaven. She could take her time finding herself a job. She had no idea what the time element for divorce might be under French law, but however long it took there had to come a time when she was free again. That was as far as she allowed her thoughts to take her. The future was a page yet to be written.

'Come on down to the boat with me,' Michael urged. 'You can't stay here on your own all day. Brenden is anxious to see you.'

There was nothing to be gained by refusal. She had given her maiden name when she checked in last night, but people here knew who she was. Already she could sense the glances, the whispered comment. As one of Noumea's most prominent citizens, Raoul could hardly hope to escape the flak. She doubted if it would bother him too much, but it bothered her.

Brenden said little beyond the initial expression of sympathy. He made lunch for the three of them, followed by a pot of his excellent coffee, then went out to clear the boot of the car ready for Michael's proposed mission.

'Are you sure about this?' Vanessa insisted as they came up on deck. 'It doesn't have to be today.'

'The sooner the better,' he said. 'Then he'll know you're not coming back.'

She gave in reluctantly. 'You know where the house is?'

He nodded. 'Brenden drove me out there the other afternoon. It's some place.'

'Isn't it just?'

Brown eyes slanted her way. 'Are you going to miss it?'

Honesty forced the admission. 'Some of it, I suppose. You can't live in the lap of luxury for any length of time without learning to take certain things for granted.' She attempted a smile. 'I'll get by. Being home again is going to be a compensation.'

'I'm coming with you,' he said. 'You do realise that?'

'Of course. There'd be no point in your staying on.' She hesitated. 'Michael . . .'

He shook his head. 'I know what you're going to say, and it doesn't make any difference. I'll be there when you need me.'

'Thanks.' She added gruffly, 'I don't deserve you.'

'I agree.' The cheerfulness was assumed. 'But then who does?'

Vanessa watched him go, too well aware that she was being totally selfish in using him as a lifeline. If she hadn't loved him enough before it was unlikely she was going to develop any deeper emotion now. He needed to cut free the way she was doing—to find himself a girl who would love him unreservedly. She would never love anyone that way. It didn't seem to be in her. In that respect if in no other, she and Raoul had been on a par.

Brenden joined her on deck a little later, bringing a rod that needed repairing. 'Had a customer took a four-hundred pounder, the other day,' he remarked. 'It didn't do my prestige any harm either.'

'So why not stay here?' Vanessa asked. 'You have your own niche—your friends.'

'The only real friends I have will be leaving,' he said without self-pity. 'When you go I do. I've already fixed all the documentation.' There was a pause while he concentrated on the job in hand. When he spoke again it was on a casual note. 'You could always come with me. The two of you, I mean. Michael was seriously considering it before this happened.'

Vanessa looked at him with lifted brows. '*Michael* was?'

'Why not? From what he tells me, there isn't a lot to drag him back to England—at least, there wasn't.' He met her eyes, smiling a little as he shook his head. 'Nothing like that. Hardly my type. He enjoys the boat, and he has enough wanderlust left in him to provide the temptation. She'll sleep three, as you know. What do you say, Van?'

It was her turn to shake her head. 'I want to go home. Is that so hard to understand?'

'No. It's just that I think you're going to be disappointed when you get there, that's all. You'll have a job, and probably a flat, and it will be back to the same old endless round. You might even think you miss the good old English weather—I've felt that way myself on odd occasions—but living with it after this won't be all that easy.'

'I'll risk it,' she said. 'Michael must please himself.'

'You know he won't do that. Not where you're concerned. Try telling him there's no future in it and he might just start living for himself.'

It was something to think about, if she could persuade him. Best for them both if the break were made now. She had to stand on her own two feet, not rely on Michael to support her, but she could only do it if he wasn't there.

He returned before three with two suitcases full of clothing but no passport.

'I tried,' he said wryly, 'but he wouldn't listen. Said if you wanted it you were to fetch it yourself.'

'You told him who you were?' Vanessa asked.

'Not only who but what. It didn't impress him one iota. The only thing he wanted to know was where you were.'

'A few minor enquiries would have provided that information easily enough if he'd been really interested,' she commented with cynicism.

'In all fairness, he knew which hotel you were booked into and that you weren't there.' Michael paused, tone altering. 'To be honest, he isn't what I expected at all. Are you sure you know what you're doing, Vanessa?'

'You want me to go back to him?' she demanded.

'I think you might have acted hastily. He seemed genuinely concerned.'

She was silent for a moment, aware of the faint leap her heart had given. 'Was there a blonde-haired woman there with him?' she asked at length. 'Around twenty-five.'

'I didn't see her.' He waited a moment himself before asking the question. 'Was she the cause?'

Vanessa bent her head. 'She's Raoul's stepsister. He was going to marry her until I ruined it all.'

'You had help. He should have kept his hands off you. Anyway, as I said, I didn't see her. We conducted the whole conversation in the library over a drink while your bags were being packed. Very civilised.'

Concentrating on the sun-dappled surface of the water, she said, 'He must realise I could go to the authorities over my passport. He doesn't have any right to hold it.'

'I doubt if he's interested in rights. He's holding it because you can't go far without it. I could see his point.'

She looked up at him then, a long searching look. 'A few days ago you were the one who wanted me to leave him.'

'A few days ago I was suffering from shock,' he admitted. 'I've had time to straighten my thoughts out since then.'

'With what conclusion?'

His gaze didn't falter although a faint flush stained his skin. 'I want you to be happy, Vanessa. If I thought I could make you happy I'd move heaven and earth. He can offer you so much more than I ever could.'

She said roughly, 'Money isn't everything.'

'It's more than money. It's a whole way of life. I never realised until I came out here just how narrow mine is.' He hesitated. 'If you really do have to get away why not do it in stages? We could fly home from Fiji as easily as from here.'

Her smile was involuntary. 'You've been bitten, haven't you? The South Seas worked its magic.'

'Something like that. It just seems an awful waste to come all this way and not see more of it.'

'What about your job?'

'I'll get another. I've been stuck too long in one spot anyway.' He paused again, watching her, a yearning in his eyes. 'What about it?'

The temptation was there undeniably, the same way it had been when Brenden had talked about it. Three months or six, home would still be there. More to the point was the fact that if she did insist on going straight back to England, Michael was going to come with her. Could she rob him of his one opportunity?

'It's too soon,' she said. 'Let me sleep on it.' She straightened away from the guard rail. 'Will you take me back to the hotel? I'd like to sort out my things.'

Michael carried her baggage up to her room when they got there, but he didn't linger, sensing her need to be alone. Vanessa spent an hour going through the contents of both suitcases, resolutely discarding those items which had not been in her original wardrobe. Later she would parcel them up and send them back to the house. What Raoul did with them was his affair.

At seven-thirty she went out for a meal, deliberately choosing one of the smaller, backstreet places where she was unlikely to be recognised. She didn't feel like eating. It was simply something to do. At this hour there were few other diners. The nearest occupied table was taken by a lone man who kept staring at her. He was dressed flashily in a cheap white seersucker suit with a black shirt beneath it. Three gold chains glinted at his throat, complementing the oily gleam of black hair. Instinctively she found herself comparing him with Raoul, feeling the ache starting deep. Last night had been bad but tonight was going to be worse; she knew it in her bones. If she could find a pharmacy still open she might be able to buy something to help her sleep.

The man followed her when she left the restaurant. Making for the busier intersection, she hailed a taxi, climbing hastily inside. He was standing on the corner looking frustrated as the vehicle moved away again. Vanessa sank back into her seat and closed her eyes, pulses still jumping. Her own fault. She should have stayed in the hotel. A woman on her own was fair game for anything.

It was almost nine before she reached her room. With the door closed and the curtains drawn over the single window, she felt cut off from the world. If she went to the islands with Brenden and Michael there would at least be no loneliness to contend with. There was a lot to be said for that factor alone.

She was on the verge of undressing when the knock came on the door. The maid with fresh towels perhaps, she thought, going to open it. Seeing Raoul standing there in the corridor froze her voice in her throat. She could only gaze at him in silence.

Raoul took the initiative, moving forward so that she was forced to step back, taking the door from her and closing it again. He was wearing a suit in mint green linen, his shirt a paler shade of the same colour. She wished suddenly and ridiculously that her erstwhile admirer from the café could see the kind of man she was accustomed to being with.

'I came earlier but you weren't here,' he said. 'You weren't at the boat either.'

Vanessa made an effort to pull herself together. 'I have to eat. What did you want?'

'To talk.' His glance went around the room, registering disparagement. 'You could have done better than this.'

'It will do, for the time I'm going to be spending in it,' she returned shortly. 'Talk about what?'

'About coming home,' he said. 'Crystal left this morning. She won't be coming back.'

'That's supposed to make everything all right again?'

He answered levelly. 'It helps.'

'Not enough.' She wanted to move away from him, but there was nowhere else to go. 'There's nothing going to alter the fact that she was with you in Tokyo.'

'I already told you what happened in Tokyo.'

'Yes, you did.' Her chin was tilted, stubbornness in its line. 'I didn't believe you then and I'm not prepared to change my mind now.'

Anger flared for a moment in his eyes. 'I could make you come with me!'

'Screaming for the police? A lot of good that would do the family name.' She stuck her hands in the pockets of her flared cotton skirt to hide their trembling, facing up to him with scornful expression. 'You can't win all the time, Raoul. You're going to have to find someone else to give you what you want. It shouldn't be difficult. You have so much to offer a woman!'

This time there was no reaction beyond the tensing of his jaw. 'Don't press me too hard,' he advised. There was a pause before he added on the same controlled note, 'So what exactly *are* you planning to do?'

'I'm going with Michael,' she said, adopting the same tone so far as she was able. 'Michael and Brenden, to be exact. We're going to take the boat across to Fiji—maybe even Tonga.'

'All arranged in one day?'

'That's right. It would be a shame not to take advantage of the opportunity while we're in this part of the world, don't you think?'

'If it's what you want then I agree you should do it.'

He put a hand to the inside pocket of his jacket and extracted a familiar black book. 'You'll need this.'

Vanessa took it from him, fingers clumsy. 'You told Michael I was going to have to fetch it.'

'What would be the use? You already told me all I needed to know. You're right, I can't hold you against your will. I'd be a fool to try. When do you plan on leaving?'

'I'm not sure.' His capitulation left her feeling curiously deflated. 'A couple of days, I imagine.'

'Do you need money?'

She shook her head. 'I still have several hundred left in the account we were using for expenses before Dad died. I can wire home for more as and when it's needed.'

'A good thing I never got around to having your assets transferred here, after all.'

'Isn't it?' They were like two strangers, she thought. She wished he would go and relieve this unbearable strain. He was so close—too close. She could catch the male scent of him, see the brown column of his throat merging with the curl of dark hair. She knew him so intimately yet she scarcely knew him at all. Her hand lifted as if to create a barrier between them, although he hadn't moved. 'It's over,' she said.

He shrugged. 'So you tell me. If you change your mind during the next couple of days you know where I am.'

Her laugh held deliberation—a will to penetrate. 'Strange, but that's exactly what Michael told me the day he arrived. I was gullible enough then to believe I owed you something. I shan't change my mind, Raoul. Not this time.'

A glint sprang in the blue eyes. 'Then we'd better say goodbye here and now.'

Vanessa took a hasty step backwards as he reached for her, but she was too late to evade his grasp. His mouth was demanding yet far from brutal, stirring her senses to life, her body to involuntary response. She wanted to cling to him, to stay with him, to forget everything that had happened. It took every ounce of willpower she possessed to break free of the embrace, with none left over to control the shakiness of her voice.

'Just go, will you, Raoul!'

He took her at her word, revealing little if any emotion. Trembling, heart heavy as lead, she forced herself to move. He wouldn't be back. She could be sure about that. She had severed the last remaining link.

There was little enough time over the following few days to brood. Vanessa welcomed the activity, the endless lists, the reorganisation of storage space and stocking-up; the plotting of a course to pick up fuel *en route*. She had never seen Michael so vitally alive as he was aboard the *Julia*. He seemed a different person.

'I might never have known what I was missing if I hadn't followed you out here,' he said the night before they were due to leave. 'It's another world.'

'There has to be a limit to how long you can spend just mooching around the South Seas,' Vanessa pointed out practically, and he smiled.

'I realise that. I'm prepared for it. But nobody will ever be able to take the memory away from me. It will be something to take out and look at on dark winter evenings when I'm home again. I'll be able to look at a map and see all those places in my mind's eye. Maybe one day I'll even repeat the experience. It depends on circumstances. A man can't walk out on responsibilities.'

'My father did,' she rejoined softly.

'Because he went against his basic nature in marrying your mother in the first place. He was a natural born loner—a rover. Probably the only reason he stayed on here so long was because he was getting older and needed to take things easier.'

She didn't dispute that assessment. In many ways he was right. Whatever else her father had been it wasn't important now. The past was dead and buried with him.

They left early on the Friday morning, heading for open sea with varying emotions. Vanessa refused to look back at the land she wouldn't be seeing again. There was no point in looking back, only forward. Determinedly cheerful, she made coffee for the three of them at ten-thirty and took it up on deck, handing each man a mug.

The sea was almost flat calm, the sunlight sparkling off the surface. 'Happy landings,' she said, sipping at the aromatic brew. 'Though I say it myself, that's pretty good coffee!'

'A bit more practice and it will be almost as good as mine,' agreed Brenden. 'We should have brought champagne.'

'Or rum.' Michael's eyes were sparkling, his whole face alight with the spirit of adventure. 'Yo-ho-ho, and all that!'

Vanessa laughed back at him, glad to see him so obviously enjoying himself. 'Pity we didn't get you a parrot and a wooden leg!'

'Talking of pirates,' said Brenden on a curious note, 'there's a boat chasing us. Can't be the coastguard because we're outside territorial waters. Think we should hove to or try to outrun him?'

The two of them turned as one to look back at the

low white craft coming up fast in their wake. Vanessa was the first to speak, her voice unsteady. 'It's the *Etoile*.' A tremor ran through her, bringing in its wake a surge of emotion so strong she could barely get the words out. 'Leave him, Bren! Let him run himself out!'

'We'd run ourselves out first,' came the rueful reply. 'Sorry, but I'm going to stop. It has to be important to get him out here on our tail.'

Vanessa said nothing because there was nothing to say. She had to see the sense in Brenden's argument. Their rate of fuel consumption was crucial to the whole voyage. Raoul's intentions were a matter for conjecture. If this was a last ditch attempt to persuade her to go back to him he was going to be disappointed.

He came alongside moments later, throwing across a rope. Dressed in white shirt and pants, his head bare in the sunlight, Raoul stepped nimbly between decks, inclining his head in Brenden's direction.

'Thanks. You saved us both a lot of time.' His eyes came back to Vanessa, ruthless in their appraisal. 'You're coming with me.'

'Just a minute.' Michael sounded totally out of his depth. 'Vanessa already told you . . .' His voice died away before the look the older man turned on him. For a long moment Michael held steady, eyes narrowing, questioning, then something in him seemed to relax suddenly. 'All right,' he said. 'I get the picture. It's up to Vanessa.'

She stared at him, unable to believe he was backing out on her. Michael lifted his shoulders, smile wry. 'We both know how we stand, Van. I already accepted it myself. You didn't really want to go to Fiji. You were doing it for my sake. Stop being so pigheaded. What do you have to lose?'

'My self-respect, for one thing,' she flashed. 'I'm not a commodity to be handed over like a sack of potatoes!'

'You're my wife,' stated Raoul. 'You belong with me. I'm not leaving without you, Vanessa. Believe me!'

'Brenden?' she appealed. 'Aren't you going to say anything?'

'I think Michael's right,' came the slow reply. 'You've been keeping it all bottled up, but I know you well enough by now to be fairly sure how you're feeling inside. Go with him. You know you want to.'

She took a deep breath, fists clenched at her sides. 'I'm not having my future decided for me by three men!'

'Two friends and a husband,' corrected Raoul. He was smiling, but the determination was still there. 'Not that I can't be a friend too.' He held out his hand to her. 'It's just a step across. You can manage that.'

'No.' She wanted desperately to give in, but some perverse instinct wouldn't allow her. 'Leave me alone, can't you!'

'No, I can't.' The words were soft. 'I need you, Vanessa.'

The fight drained from her suddenly. She looked at him with darkened eyes. Need, not love. Yet it could be an adequate substitute given other factors in common. They needed each other, if it came to that. He had spoiled her for any other man.

Michael broke the silence. 'I think you just got your answer.'

The leavetakings were painful. There might come a time when they would all meet up again, but it was doubtful. Standing in the after-well as Raoul brought the boat round in a wide arc, Vanessa wondered how long it would be before Michael began to tire of aimless wandering. She gave him six months at the most. She watched until the *Julia* was out of sight before turning slowly back to where Raoul stood at the wheel.

'How did you know we were leaving today?'

He gave her a smiling glance. 'I made it my business to find out. I was going to get you off that boat whatever it took.'

'I thought I'd never see you again,' she said huskily. 'Did you know the other night that you weren't going to let me go?'

'I knew. What I had to find was a way of keeping you here. In the end there was only one way.' He added levelly, 'We're going to Royale.'

Breathing space he'd called it not so long ago. It applied even more now. Perhaps if they started again from square one and got to know each other a little better they might find a deeper commitment. Mutual trust was the first priority.

'I shouldn't ask,' she said, 'but did Crystal really go for good?'

His expression hardened fractionally. 'This time, yes. You'll find no trace of her at Royale. She took everything.'

'Twenty years is a long time.'

'She destroyed them all in the end. I can't feel anything for her.' He paused, tone altering. 'Do you still believe I was lying about Tokyo?'

'Not now,' she admitted. 'She mightn't have felt quite so vindictive if you had made love to her.'

'Is that a criticism?'

'Just an observation. You said it yourself—"hell hath no fury like a woman scorned".'

'So perhaps I wasn't without fault. It makes little

difference now.' He was looking ahead. 'There's
Royale.'

Vanessa watched the island grow, picking out
familiar detail. She had a glimpse of the little cove
between the two spurs of rock as they came in, then
they were manoeuvring alongside the jetty, engine
cut, coming to rest with a gentle bump and a slapping
of waves against the hull.

Raoul was first ashore to secure their mooring. He
made no attempt to touch her until they reached solid
ground, taking her arm as she began to move in the
direction of the house, and turning her along the
shoreline.

'Not that way,' he said, 'this. There are things we
still have to talk about, and only one place to do it.'

The little hut was unchanged, its sandy floor
smooth and unblemished. Vanessa was reticent at first,
but not for long, shedding restraint along with each
garment, eager for his lips, his hands, the hard weight
of his body. She had so nearly lost this man of hers. It
didn't bear thinking about.

He took her with a fierceness that matched her own,
sinking down afterwards with his dark head on her
breast and his arms still wrapping her close.

'I love you,' he murmured. 'Dear God, how I love
you! There hasn't been one solitary waking moment
these past few days when I haven't wanted to come
and get you.'

Her own voice was shaky. 'If you'd said that earlier
you'd have got me off the boat a whole lot quicker.
When did you know?'

'In Tokyo for certain. I could only hope it wasn't
too late to rouse you to the same emotion.'

'I beat you to it,' she said. 'I fell in love with you
right here in this hut months ago, only I wouldn't

admit it even to myself at the time because I was afraid of getting hurt.' She touched his face, eyes misty. 'I gave up hope this morning when we sailed. The worst part was knowing I only had myself to blame for sending you away the other night. When I think how close we came to . . .'

'It didn't happen, that's all that matters.' He lifted his head to kiss her nipple, smiling at the ready response. 'And they say English women are frigid!'

'When all we need is a Frenchman!' She looked into those blue, blue eyes and felt emotion swathe her heart. 'I love you so much, Raoul. I'd say it in French if I thought the sentiment would survive my accent.'

'It will improve,' he said. 'Until then I can bear it in English.' He sought her mouth, cherishing it with a tenderness that spoke volumes. 'We should take care,' he murmured thickly as passion grew again between them. 'We agreed to wait a while.'

'I don't want to wait,' she whispered, reaching for him hungrily. 'Not anymore.'

The white boat paralleled the shore line, heading west at a fair rate of knots. Watching it from the balcony, Vanessa said tentatively, 'You know, that looks like the *Julia*.'

Raoul came to the bedroom doorway behind her to take a look, shaking his head in derision. 'Too small, and her superstructure is lower. Anyway, Brenden was still in Tahiti less than a week ago. He'd need wings!'

'Wishful thinking,' she acknowledged. 'I suppose he may pay us a visit one of these fine days.'

'In the meantime, you can console yourself with an old flame,' on a faint note of irony. 'Only take care how you greet him tonight. French women are notoriously possessive wives.'

Vanessa laughed. 'Who would have imagined Michael would find himself a French girl in Tonga, of all places? To say nothing of a job!' She turned her head to glance at the dark-haired man who had come to stand beside her at the rail, her senses registering how little difference two years had made to the effect he had on her. 'Thanks to you.'

'I only supplied the introduction. The rest was up to him.' A smile flicked the corners of his mouth. 'I had no hand in finding the girl.'

'I should hope not too. Some things can't be arranged.' She slid an arm about the lean waist, leaning her head against one broad shoulder with a small sigh of contentment. 'I only hope they're as lucky as we've been.'

'More than luck,' Raoul said lightly, dropping a kiss on the top of her head. 'Extremely good management. I always knew you had it in you to play your part with enough encouragement, now here you are, one of Noumea's most popular hostesses, or so I'm reliably told.'

'Don't forget my other accomplishment,' she rejoined, looking down to the sweeping lawns where their toddler son played happily with his young nanny. 'Not that you can't take a little of the credit there too, I suppose.'

Raoul laughed. 'He may be all French in looks, but he has his mother's English spirit. Very little daunts him.'

'You almost daunted me,' she said. 'Two years ago I could never have visualised a time like this.' She paused before adding softly, 'I don't think we should leave it too long to supply Real with a brother or sister, do you?'

The hand caressing her nape stopped moving for a

moment as he looked down at her. When he answered his voice held a new note. 'I agree.'

Vanessa balked as he turned her towards the sliding doors, laughingly protesting. 'I didn't mean right now! I still have to change for lunch!'

Blue eyes glinted as he swung her up from the floor. 'Lunch isn't for another hour, and this is only a rehearsal. We have to be sure to get it right on the night.'

Take 4
Exciting Books
Absolutely
FREE

Love, romance, intrigue... all are captured for you by Mills & Boon's top-selling authors. By becoming a regular reader of Mills & Boon's Romances you can enjoy 6 superb new titles every month plus a whole range of special benefits: your very own personal membership card, a free monthly newsletter packed with recipes, competitions, exclusive book offers and a monthly guide to the stars, plus extra bargain offers and big cash savings.

AND an Introductory FREE GIFT for YOU.
Turn over the page for details.

As a special introduction we will send you four
exciting Mills & Boon Romances Free and
without obligation when you complete
and return this coupon.

At the same time we will reserve a subscription to
Mills & Boon Reader Service for you. Every month,
you will receive 6 of the very latest novels by leading
Romantic Fiction authors, delivered direct to your
door. You don't pay extra for delivery — postage and
packing is always completely Free. There is no
obligation or commitment — you can cancel your
subscription at any time.

You have nothing to lose and a whole world of
romance to gain.

Just fill in and post the coupon today to **MILLS & BOON
READER SERVICE, FREEPOST, P.O. BOX 236, CROYDON,
SURREY CR9 9EL.**

**Please Note:- READERS IN SOUTH AFRICA write to
Mills & Boon, Postbag X3010,
Randburg 2125, S. Africa.**

FREE BOOKS CERTIFICATE

**To: Mills & Boon Reader Service, FREEPOST, P.O. Box 236,
Croydon, Surrey CR9 9EL.**

Please send me, free and without obligation, four Mills & Boon Romances, and reserve a
Reader Service Subscription for me. If I decide to subscribe I shall, from the beginning of the
month following my free parcel of books, receive six new books each month for £6.60. post
and packing free. If I decide not to subscribe, I shall write to you within 10 days. The free
books are mine to keep in any case. I understand that I may cancel my subscription at any
time simply by writing to you. I am over 18 years of age

Please write in BLOCK CAPITALS

Signature _____   _____

Name _____

Address _____

_____Post code _____

SEND NO MONEY — TAKE NO RISKS.

Please don't forget to include your Postcode.

*Remember, postcodes speed delivery Offer applies in UK only and is not valid
to present subscribers Mills & Boon reserve the right to exercise discretion in
granting membership If price changes are necessary you will be notified*

6R   *Offer expires 31st December 1985*

EP